Sacred
Sexuality
WITHIN & BETWEEN

Julie Elizabeth

SACRED SEXUALITY:
Within & Between

Copyright © 2022 by Julie Elizabeth

To request permissions, contact the publisher at
contact@freedomhousepublishingco.com or julie3mft@gmail.com
Hardcover ISBN: 978-1-952566-74-5
Paperback ISBN: 978-1-952566-71-4
Ebook ISBN: 978-1-952566-72-1
Printed in the USA.
Freedom House Publishing Co
Middleton, ID 83644
www.freedomhousepublishingco.com

FREEDOM HOUSE
PUBLISHING CO

For all of my teachers- my lovers,
mirrors, mentors, ancestors, angels,
role models, and sexual pioneers;
For all of the people who have loved me
into being who I am today
- thank you.

Sacred Sexuality

TABLE OF CONTENTS

INTRODUCTION

Spirituality is an interesting topic to tackle. As conscious beings, we always want to hit it with logic. With science. With evidence. But the thing is, it's beautifully mysterious. It is in our nature to contemplate our own existence and try to make sense of everything, but in our effort to cope with the uncertainty, humanity has made a major error in my opinion. We started pretending to have the answers instead of remaining in marvelous curiosity of the unknowable, the unmeasurable, and the unexplainable. I believe we are the closest to having it figured out when we can accept that we don't really "know" anything. Then we can acknowledge the discomfort and vulnerability that comes with uncertainty and learn to live with it more healthily. If we don't, we become susceptible to quick fixes or dependency, turning to external sources of authority for answers and a false sense of security. We give away our power when we abandon our own inner voice of authority and run fearfully from the insecurity of not knowing. Layers worth noting include religious conditioning and the inherited impact of centuries of abuse of power and control from the patriarchy. I'm not sure which came first—the good intention and light and truth that religion does possess or the systems of fear-based control and compliance that exploit innocence in order to maintain power and repress the voices of those in its congregations. Part of reclaiming my authentic spiritual identity was starting over with an existential crisis and sitting with uncertainty. I went back to ground zero and gave myself permission to question everything. It was immensely uncomfortable. And it was the best worst thing that ever happened to me.

When I was able to break down everything I had been taught to believe and consider what really felt like truth to me, it allowed me to find my inner voice and intuition. I started exercising the muscle of discernment. I learned to lean into it, listen to it, and trust it. Isn't that the basis of the scientific method—to question everything? I conducted my own case study experiment and developed methods for discerning. If something caused shame, it was worth investigating. I would challenge any distortion in my belief system that was not in alignment with compassion for myself and others. Compassion is a misunderstood concept, as many people view it as permissive, weak, or lacking boundaries. When it is not balanced with integrity, it can lead to over-giving, making excuses, and people-pleasing. But I believe compassion in its truest form actually allows us to have more accountability within ourselves and from others. True compassion creates opportunities for more love. In my process, I started questioning anything that wasn't in alignment with my new definition of God.

This became the foundation I used to explore my authentic identity, relationships, and sexuality. I know it's scary to approach the subject of sexuality, especially in the context of spirituality. I know it can be painful for so many women and people. I know how confusing it can be to explore your own sexuality in a context of competing messages and shameful conditioning. I see you, I am you, you are me, we're in this together, and I love you. With that being said, in this book I want to acknowledge that it is a process and a journey of healing, rewiring, and corrective experiencing. Every person's experience will have elements that are absolutely unique, so no two stories will be the same. Your path toward reclaiming your own pleasure and defining your own sexual identity is up to you and only you. You are the expert on your life journey, so you are the only one who can define truth as you go through this process of self-inquiry and introspective discovery. I'm here to share my truth from my own lived experiences in hopes that you will find something useful or at least feel less lonely.

What were you taught about sex? What made you pick up this book? How do you feel when you think about reclaiming your sexual pleasure and solo sexual activity? What have you been told about sexuality in the context of spirituality? Taking this kind of inventory can be a beautiful way to begin observing your experience and recognizing that anything you believe is something that was learned and conditioned based on your life experiences. You get to choose which ones to keep and which ones to replace with something more consistent with how you want to live and who you want to be. For me, I use a guide to help me discern truth from distortions as I create my reality. Every time, I find wisdom in my body. I have learned to redefine the relationship with my body and instead of being at war with it—criticizing it for not fitting into the unrealistic, contradictory, and impossible mold society gave me—I have learned to listen and appreciate the incredible tool of magic that it is. It will tell me what is a clear yes and what isn't. The most difficult part is learning to listen and trust it.

I grew up in what I would consider a very sex negative culture. Most of what I learned focused on strict abstinence and consequences if the conditions were violated. Sex was only something to be done between a man and a woman after they were married. If not within those conditions, sex was viewed as sinful, slutty, dirty, shameful, and irreversible, and it made you less worthy. In the religious context I was raised in, sex outside of marriage disqualified you

3

from being in the presence of God. It was taught that you would have a spiritual death and the severity of that sin was second to murder. Heavy stuff for a teenager. There were a lot of double standards and confusing narratives in the world around me. My family would joke about sex like it was a taboo topic that was funny to reference and giggle about, like they had some kind of insider secret. At the same time, my body was hyper-monitored and controlled with specific measurements of how much skin could show to be deemed appropriate. If too much skin was showing, I would be responsible for being too provocative and boys might have inappropriate thoughts about me. How dare I disrespect them like that? Modesty was an absolute priority. Our bodies were temples and had to be kept clean. Therefore, anything of sexual nature was dirty.

Body image is a big part of what separates us from our bodies and our power of sacred sexuality. It makes us enemies with our bodies instead of lovers, best friends, and lifelong companions. Then come social expectations, gender roles, and cultural narratives that teach us how to fit in instead of how to stand out and celebrate our unique, authentic expressions. We become distracted with chasing all the things we're told we're supposed to be instead of cultivating the art of simply being, creating, and expressing in our truth.

I personally identify as a woman and use she/her pronouns. Since this book is based on insights from my personal lived experiences, the language used will be predominantly speaking to my experience as a cisgendered woman with female anatomy, with references to generalized cultural and societal experiences of people who identify as women. I'd like to recognize that these examples are not representative of all women. I acknowledge gender as a spectrum of self-expression and identity. It is more than boxes or labels with two polarized extremes that have been socially constructed based on roles and expectations associated with biological sex or anatomy. In my own expression, I have found healing and authenticity through integrating both feminine and masculine aspects of my identity. I also identify as sexually fluid with predominantly heterosexual experiences. The language used throughout this book will reflect my experiences in relationships with mostly male partners and cisgendered anatomy. I'd like to acknowledge that physical anatomy is a single dimension of the human experience. I hope that any male bodied, transgender, gender fluid, non-binary, and LGBTQ+ readers feel included and empowered in your own experience and expression of feminine and masculine energies, and that you find value in the principles of my experiences, regardless of your anatomy. I know that people in minority groups are often not represented in the mainstream narrative. I see you and hope you find love, acceptance, peace, healing, and pleasure on your journey with your body through your own exploration of authentic expression, sensuality, and sexual identity.

For many women, we become disconnected from our bodies at a very young age. We get distracted by external standards of beauty and conforming to societal expectations of what we're supposed to look like. This disconnects us from ourselves as we try to fit in, chasing a feeling of acceptance and belonging. This is related to developmental concepts of socialization and social mirroring, which begin in infancy to help babies connect with their environment and adapt socially. It's not always conscious so we often don't realize that we are doing it, especially as kids when it's purely instinctual. We build our worldview based on what we see, what our brains and bodies absorb, and start adaptively responding. This socialization process is what people are referring to when they use the word "conditioning." When we internalize a certain understanding and begin using it to navigate the world, it is met with a response or a consequence. This is how we learn. The thoughts, beliefs, and behavior patterns we develop are largely a result of social learning as we absorb spoken and unspoken rules of our environment and their consequences. So much of this process is automatic as we are growing up and having experiences that teach us what to expect from the world and what the world expects from us. It's important to understand that none of this is our fault. When we are children, the world is what it is and we learn how to adjust and live in it. As evolutionary beings, we are wired this way to help us interact with our environment and survive. The most beautiful part is that we never stop learning. We never stop evolving. The culture we were raised in was socially constructed by adults who were operating in their imperfect human nature based on what they had experienced, what they knew, and what they had the capacity to do.

Why is this relevant? It's important to understand how you may have developed the belief system you have around sexuality, body image, spirituality, and your sense of self. All of these categories are shaped by our social experiences that can reinforce beliefs, whether they are true or not. To begin accessing more of our power, we must realize that we are culture. We create it, we sustain it, and we can change it. Change is a natural part of life, and from generation to generation, we continue to learn and grow to the best of our ability. As Maya Angelou said, "Do the best you can until you know better. Then when you know better, do better." That's what this book is about—expressing my own truth to help change the culture around sexuality and help women reconnect with their bodies, their pleasure, their power, their creativity, their spiritual gifts, and themselves.

We don't realize we're already beautiful and perfect. Our uniqueness is our gift and our expression is our craft. It's not a competition. There is room for everyone to contribute and build and share beauty and truth and love in the world. More love breeds more love. This is the concept of abundance and freedom. Fear causes contraction, hoarding, possession, competition, and control tactics. It's common to experience anger, hurt, resentment, and shame when witnessing the ways that mistruths were internalized and caused you pain. It may be helpful to remind yourself that by allowing yourself to feel those things, express them, and release them, you will find what you need to heal and begin to reclaim your power. There is power in feeling, witnessing, accepting, surrendering, forgiving, and transmuting pain into resilience. My hope is that in reading this book, to some minute degree, you will be able to see yourself more clearly and love yourself more deeply. I hope that you will discover some aspect of yourself that has been longing to connect with you, and I wish for you the most beautiful reunion of coming home to yourself.

As you take in new perspectives about these topics, I invite you to simply notice the feelings, thoughts, or body sensations that arise without judgment. Get curious about them. Simply noticing them and allowing them to be felt can help you discern what *you* believe to be true and if any of your conditioned beliefs might need to be unlearned or updated. As an adult, you have the power to examine your beliefs and choose for yourself what you would like to keep or replace. Whether you have painful or blissful sensations, I encourage you to maintain compassion for all of your experience. You are beautiful and perfectly imperfect wherever you are on your journey.

As I wrote this book, I discovered that I have many versions of authentic expression and how I've learned to define truth. I will be sharing from several angles as I allowed my authentic expression to come through. Some sections are written from my analytical and logical masculine. Others are written from raw experiences with feeling and creative expression. I hope this message reaches my right-brain readers and my left-brain readers. Either way, please know all of it has come from my heart and is a result of my own lived experiences. So, from my heart to yours, thank you for taking the time to witness my truth. I wish you growth, healing, and joy as you discover your own.

RESTORING TRUTH

More and more I'm beginning to see that life is just a series of choices. This is the true gift of agency. We get to choose how to respond in any given moment. There's so much we don't have control over, but in my experience, when I have felt the most disempowered is when I have power I'm not realizing. One of the most life-changing examples is the power to choose what I believe. Not what I think, not what I feel, not what happens to me—I get to choose what I believe. What I accept as truth at the core of me. This is the same power that allows me to create my reality. Now that I understand this, it's not a matter of if, but how. I can choose to create my reality either consciously or unconsciously. I much prefer to do it consciously, as my unconscious patterns are more painful and create a lot of suffering.

Discernment is one key. How do I define truth for myself? There have been many principles from religion that I chose to either redefine or keep. Among these is a bible verse, "by their fruits ye shall know them." I believe this applies to more than just prophets or people. I believe this applies to principles and teachings, narratives from culture or society. If God is love, anything that is not in alignment with love is not of God. If I have a belief from what I've been taught, and it causes me great shame, this is a signal I need to investigate. I need to adjust or replace it with a more loving thing.

Any internalized belief that disconnects me from myself, from my intuition, or from being loved unconditionally is distorted. Does it create judgment, shame, confusion, resentment, fear, powerlessness, despair, or unease?

There is a principle from Internal Family Systems, a therapy model developed by Dr. Richard Schwartz, that suggests our inner divinity or highest Self is defined by eight qualities: calmness, clarity, compassion, curiosity, creativity, courage, confidence, connectedness. As I have explored this concept in my own experiences, these principles resonate as indicators that I am connected to my higher Self, my inner divinity. As a discernment practice, I pay attention to my body. What am I feeling and where am I feeling it? I access my observer stance with curiosity and compassion and practice nonjudgmental awareness, simply noticing. Can I operate from a place of Self and identify what beliefs are contributing most to my suffering? What do those parts of me need for healing? Beliefs that cause shame are not true. Shame is an alarm bell for "not true." The truth is not always comfortable, but paired with compassion, it leads to peace, love, joy, pleasure, gratitude, and relief. The goal is not to rid life of discomfort or suffering entirely. We will never reach alignment with perfect truth. We just get to say yes to the practice of unlearning and not accepting anything that is not in alignment with truth. Life is a process of becoming. It takes a lifetime (maybe many lifetimes) to practice becoming One with God and embodying true unconditional love.

The other (I would argue most important) key is surrender. We must have courage to surrender to agonizing pain and allow it in again and again. Accept that suffering is the only way to a liberated self. I know, I know, it sounds super depressing. But there's a silver lining. Accepting our suffering and surrendering to feeling through the pain leads us to liberation and the other side of the coin. It allows us to

10

accept the parts of ourselves that we reject to heal them with love from ourselves and from the Divine. Love, healing, freedom, pleasure, and joy are the other side of the coin. There can be a purpose to our pain, helping us live a full life, learning and growing through our experiences, and returning to love again and again as we evolve and expand.

Sexuality is one of our most powerful gifts. Everything we are taught in society about it is almost precisely the opposite of truth. Think about it—the majority of people are taught to be afraid of it, not discuss it, suppress it, or reject it. Whether it's explicitly stated or implied, there are rules around it, designed to contain and control the power that comes from it. Whether this is a simple byproduct of fear, ignorance, or willful control and manipulation, it's important that the truth be known. We must dig beneath all the conditioned knee-jerk responses reinforced by discomfort and liberate the truth.

The truth is we are powerful in our pleasure. We are infinitely capable of creating, healing, growing, and expanding beyond measure when we are following our pleasure. Of course, that sounds provocative, like I'm suggesting pleasure is all that matters. It's not. But the pendulum has swung far too much and it's time for a reclamation of our true nature. Anything that causes shame or unfounded fear is not based in truth or light. Somehow, sexuality has become so deeply entrenched in shame that the truth has become buried in darkness. Why would something have such a powerful force of repression and discomfort working against it? Because there is an incredible power there. There is magic in it. It is a precious gift that is completely free and available within our own bodies and sovereignty poses a threat to authority. I know this starts to sound like a conspiracy, because it is. Quite literally. For centuries, it has been intentionally targeted in society by power-seeking men afraid of losing control. They felt threatened, consumed by insecurity.

How could they stay in control if everyone was connected to their own magic? What would happen if there was not a façade or distorted version of reality that convinced them they were powerless and needed something outside themselves to survive? So, what better weapons to disarm people from their power than fear and shame? And what better way than using the very thing that is the source of power to harm and assign blame? Religion is the same and it is often the source of so much social pain and shame related to both sex and spirituality. It was a man-made game.

Sexual power can harm or heal. Spiritual power can harm or heal. Where there is duality and polarity in all things, choice reigns supreme. We all possess the power of choice. Many concepts have become corrupt in the way they're presented. It's not that religion lacks truth, the institution just distorts it to serve its own interests. I heard a quote from Aubry Marcus that has stuck with me: "The goal of propaganda is not to replace truth with a lie, but to confuse the notion of truthfulness to the extent that everyone gives up on looking for it." Confusion can be a powerful weapon too. Especially paired with fear, it creates division within ourselves and between us as a community.

The way sexuality and spirituality are taught in our society causes harm. From repression to victim blaming to control and manipulation, most people are not supported with the information or tools needed to have healthy relationships with these concepts. Can there be one without the other? I would argue they are very much interconnected.

While there is darkness around both of these topics, it doesn't serve us to fear the darkness and abandon our light in the same stride. I've discovered there can be righteous and rightful rebellion in reclaiming sexual power—using it to liberate love, joy, beauty, spirituality, connection, creativity, and play. All of these things can stand on their own in protest of the untruths that plague our culture. We can allow it to be an innocent, beautiful celebration of life. Even in healing, there is so much potential for reversing the impact of harm that has been caused by dark forces and abused by those misusing their power over others. Consent is key. Deep healing can be found through shadow play and riding the pendulum swing. There can be corrective experiences for our bodies by "playing" with power dynamics, fantasy, role play, energetic archetypes, intentionality, or affirmations. It all becomes real when we bring it into the physical realm and allow our bodies to experience it as true. There are infinite possibilities that can be explored through sexuality. Our bodies are designed to create life, love, and beauty. But don't just take my word for it. I invite you to unlock the wisdom of your body, develop a relationship with it—all of it—and learn to listen to it, trust it, and discover the truth of who you are as a divine spiritual being in a beautifully complex physical vessel with deeply embedded gifts.

PART ONE

SPIRITUALITY

DISCERNMENT:
INTUITION IS VOICE OF AUTHORITY

———— $\cdot\!\!\sim\!\!\diamond\!\!\sim\!\!\cdot$ ————

The first step to defining my authentic spirituality was establishing my own inner voice of authority. I had to forgive myself for believing so blindly and for allowing others to tell me what spirituality should be. I was a child; I had no way of knowing. I trusted because I didn't know anything different. I had taken to heart the idea that my parents, men, prophets, and leaders in the church were more connected than me. In my religious culture, if I had doubts or feelings, I was taught to question them and dismiss them. There were mixed messages, which was confusing. I was taught to pray and ask God if something was true, but there really wasn't support or room to get an answer that derailed from the mainstream narrative that the institution approved. I didn't have the support I needed to trust my intuition, my heart, and my inner knowing. I learned to doubt myself instead and was quick to assume I was the problem and I must have gotten it wrong. This is why the structure, culture, and institution of religions built around patriarchy is abusive. It systemically gaslights women. I was disconnected from my body, my pleasure, and my sensuality, which are some of the most powerful ways God speaks to me directly and essential tools for my healing and resilience building. It's no surprise I was susceptible to spiritual abuse; I was groomed for it. I was raised without knowing how to access my own power.

There was also dysfunction in my home environment that amplified and perpetuated the problem. So much of my suffering in my upbringing was caused by me not being properly equipped—not knowing what I didn't know. This book is for anyone who's like me and didn't know or doesn't know where your power is. If you've been hurt like I was, I'm so sorry that happened to you. It wasn't your fault, and I see you. You are not alone. I love you. We are all connected as humans and together we can heal and create something new. This book is for me, and this book is for you.

After "following the prophet" and doing what I was told, there were choices I had made that were not aligned for me. They didn't feel true to my heart, and they weren't making me happy. When I realized this, I made a vow to myself to create a life that was more authentic to who I am. I started by stopping anything that wasn't true to me, and stopped trying to force myself to be what I was *supposed* to be. I gave myself permission to start questioning everything and only did things that really felt meaningful to me. That didn't mean only eating ice cream, neglecting responsibilities, or becoming selfish and uncaring—that wouldn't be true to my heart.

This was terrifying to me because I had been taught to fear "the natural man." I had been taught that my natural urges, desires, or tendencies were an enemy to God. I realize all things can have many meanings based on how we interpret or perceive them, but this one was talked about and reinforced often. I was taught to believe that God wanted and required me to be and do very specific things to be worthy. I hadn't considered that I could trust my inherent, natural self to be good, loving, intuitive, wise, connected, and divine. The identity of being human was so closely tied to the idea that we are sinful by nature and need to be saved from ourselves. How different the narrative would have been if it wasn't drenched in shame and instead it was normalized that part of learning is making mistakes! That mistakes don't make us wrong or dirty, it simply means we have freedom to make choices that have consequences, which are tools to help us develop and grow. And yes, just as children need support and help as they make mistakes, so do we. The kind of support they need is not fear and shame, but a response that is loving, helpful, and encouraging! What if the narrative about God as a parental power was one of unconditional love? That is the godly parent my inner child needed and deserved.

My life would have looked so very different if I had known I could trust my body, my heart, and my intuition to guide me; if I had known God would always love me and be a place I could turn for comfort, clarity, support, and wisdom. It took me 30 years to reverse the damage that was caused by the culture of shame and spiritual abuse of an institutional God. And I'm still not done. It's something I work on every day as I cultivate my relationship with myself, my spirituality, and the world around me. I can't undo the pain; I can't change the past or erase the conditioning. But I can use it to fuel me. I can transmute it back into power as I tell my story and create change.

I see now that I am still that inner child on a journey of learning and growing and making mistakes. I no longer fear them. My mistakes are valued lessons that I thank God for every day. Each one is an opportunity to learn from the consequences of my choices that provide information and experiences I need to find my balance and keep moving. When I am not living my life in fear and shame, I am much more capable of taking accountability for my actions and working to stay in alignment with my values and integrity. For me, balance is a key principle to everything. We often perceive the world in extremes and duality, like right vs. wrong, black vs. white, good vs. bad, happy vs. sad. But life is more than one or the other. We exist in a world full of gray and color, with a spectrum to everything. Maybe there isn't a right or wrong way to live unequivocally. Maybe truth is subjective to each person individually as they navigate their journey, learn their lessons, and experience the consequences of their actions. Maybe it just depends. Maybe it's more than any of us can fully understand, because it's bigger than us. Maybe the impact our choices have on the collective that we are all a part of is more than we can fathom.

As an adult, I realized I didn't need any other authority than myself and discovered the ways I was able to commune with a higher power directly. Not only that, but it opened up an entire universe of exploration and possibility. Truth is infinite and can't possibly be fathomed within a single person, organization, or lifetime. We spend our entire lives learning, exploring, and discovering. Just like science. Truth is relative—we go with our best understanding of things and remain open to questioning forever and ever. Things of the spiritual realm are no different. We are all students of life. The mysteries of the universe are expansive and vast. I can shrink back in fear of not knowing or I can marvel at the beauty and depth of the mystery and enjoy the excitement of discovering.

It's easy to contemplate the complexities and see the uncertainties of life. It can also be overwhelming and uncomfortable to not have the answers to everything. I know it can be scary for me sometimes, especially when having answers growing up meant predictability, control, and a sense of security, however delusional that may have been. But I've realized I would much rather have the uncertainty because uncertainty leaves room for possibility, wonder, imagination, and curiosity. It leaves room for questions, spaciousness, and dreams. I would much rather recognize I don't actually *know* anything, so I can always be open to learning. This provides a different sense of security, strangely. Once I accepted that there is more to this life than I can ever see, it gave me this new ability to breathe and have flexibility and adaptability. When I adopt a definition of truth as having some degree of relativity, I don't have to cling to it. I can be present in this moment with what feels true to me. And I can release the need to know everything. All I have is this moment anyway, so if I live with a commitment to discovering, exploring, questioning, and staying open to receiving what life has to offer me, I am filled with peace.

So, how do I determine what truth feels like to me? It's a combination of things I have reclaimed, discovered, and tested along the way. One of the most powerful tools for discernment is through my body. My body is where God, or the universe, speaks to me. I feel peace, ease, clarity, and joy in my body. There is a lightness in my heart and I am usually filled with energy. Depending on what I'm discerning, I might experience a calm, quiet, profound sense of peace and grounding, or I'll experience an energetic, exciting, intense, loud "YES" that usually leads to dancing, giggling, or a call to take an aligned action on a specific thing. I had to practice to learn these things—how to ask my body, how to go within, and how to take risks to act on the feelings that came. I built trust with my intuition as the results and miracles started to happen. It's still a process I work to develop and fine-tune as I continue to lean in, get vulnerable, and trust myself. From there, I let my practice expand and, as my friend Angel says, I let myself "go in and go up." Once I repaired the trust in myself as an inner voice of authority, I felt ready to start building a relationship with sources outside myself.

SPIRITUAL
RECLAMATION

The religious system hurt me. I don't say that as a victim or from a place of resentment anymore, but it is a fact. It doesn't mean there isn't beauty in that same system, as in most things there is light and dark. For me and my truth, there was not enough light to make it worth staying. I followed my path to a freer forum of spirituality outside of religion. I see it now as something I can appreciate for the sake of language, conceptual philosophy, and a mark of human history as people have made efforts to make meaning of our collective existence with traditions of ceremony and rituals for sacred things. I take what resonates as truth and leave what doesn't. Truth is such a relative concept. It's hard to define without the power of personal discernment. It took a while for me to reach this place of acceptance and openness. For a long time, I didn't have the tools to protect myself from false truths or distortions. It was a painful part of my journey, but one that I am grateful for. If not for the pain caused by those experiences, I may not have been so diligent in defining what is true for me. I may have stayed in comfortability and blindly accepted what was taught to me. Through this process, I have a new relationship with pain. I no longer avoid it, run from it, or numb it. I see the value and purpose in my pain as a necessary part of life with lessons and hidden gifts. I look back on my life and see the things that caused the greatest shame have now become my greatest sources of strength.

I was raised in a culture that taught me God's love is conditional. I was taught how many ways I could be unworthy of His love. Yes, *His*. I was taught God is a male father figure who cuts you off from His presence when you disappoint Him. And to earn grace and forgiveness, you have to repent and come with a "broken heart and contrite spirit." There is a female counterpart, Heavenly Mother, who is never spoken about and therefore absent in any kind of relationship that inspires divine revelation. The Divine Feminine was deeply repressed, silenced, controlled, and manipulated by the patriarchy and paired with a narrative that it was to protect Her. It was out of respect for Her? That is how we show respect for women? We tell them what to do with their bodies, how to follow leadership, and we don't listen to them? Nope. Nope. Nope. I call bullshit. This seems like a very effective structure for obedience, control, and manipulation of power by men and it disconnects everyone from the true love of the Divine Masculine.

I discovered my own truth through experiencing the results of untruth. See, I believed the narrative as a young, impressionable child. I took it to heart and wanted to please God. I wanted Him to be proud of me, to love me, and to accept me. What kind of parent turns away when their child makes a mistake? What kind of parent withdraws from their child when they aren't perfect? What kind of father would allow his daughter to receive this as a model of what love looks like and teach her to accept this kind of treatment from men? And what kind of husband would keep his wife silent, hidden behind him, claiming it was for her own good that she is not heard or seen? That is not a God I respect or believe in.

I see the blatant errors in what I was taught. Some might say my criticism is unholy, sacrilegious, and dare I say the "F" word... feminist? People might wonder why feminists are so angry. Is it because we hate men? We want to flip the scales and have the power to ourselves and make men suffer and feel small out of revenge for centuries of repression? I mean, I'd be lying if I said that didn't sound appealing from time to time after I became fully aware of how egregious the injustices have been. But in reality, my anger has been doing the very thing it is designed to do. Its purpose is to help me set boundaries and orient to my needs. In this case, my needs are quite simple—equality, respect, dignity, and sovereignty.

I think many people misunderstand and get defensive, claiming women are different from men and that should be celebrated! To those people, I'd like to offer some clarity from my own truth and perspective. First of all, there are layers to this. Gender roles and expectations based on biological sex and anatomy dictating whether I should be feminine or masculine are deeply flawed. I value the polarity and duality of the feminine and masculine, and I agree those differences should be celebrated! I don't agree that the masculine can only be held by men and the feminine by women. I'm not even making an argument here for transgender or gender fluid individuals, though I am a strong advocate for inclusivity, acceptance, and validation of a person's right to identify as they see fit. The point I would like to make is that we all possess these energies and traits because we are all interconnected with life and the universe. Religion claims we are children of God—a Father and Mother, or the Divine Masculine and Divine Feminine. If we are born of the same process, just as our genes contain material from both parents, why would our energetic body be any different? It just makes sense.

Gender is a social construct that dictates what men are supposed to be and do and what women are supposed to be and do. I believe gender got distorted and warped through misinterpretation of the polarity principle that suggests there is power in having differences. Polarity provides contrast, which creates a beautiful energetic attraction and charge that can be quite powerful. I also believe there are many nuances in how these energies can manifest. There are many facets to each side, but the most important piece is that we have all of the elements inside us. Females have masculine, males have feminine. Everyone can fall on a spectrum of which feels more dominant, or equal, and it can fluctuate through life phases and identity development! For myself, I am biologically female and identify as a woman with a dominant feminine essence, as well as a strong masculine essence. I value both as essential components to my identity as a whole.

Now, back to equality. I don't want the interpretation of equality to imply I'm the same as a man. I do believe we should rid ourselves of expectations and allow people to be who they authentically are and find the roles and expressions that fit them best. The power of polarity can show up in a lot of different ways and women, men, non-binary, transgender, or gender fluid individuals can create numerous combinations that form beautiful, energetically dynamic relationships in a variety of constellations. I understand this topic can be quite complex, which is why I choose to view it simply. Treat people with equal respect, dignity, and consideration. Don't make assumptions about them and who they should be or what they are capable of. Recognize that even in polarity, leadership and power can be shared between individuals and is actually more balanced when each person maintains personal power and sovereignty over themselves. Neither feminine or masculine is better than the other. Both are essential for balance. Both must be valued and respected.

As for God? I don't subscribe to the Heavenly Father of my childhood. He was not loving. In fact, the version of God that was presented to me was cold, distant, and conditional. He needed me to earn approval and required me to fear upsetting him and risk suffering consequences that seemed like an angry punishment. He was a God that would give the silent treatment and abandon you if you were not worthy of His love. A God that condones the way women are repressed, men are controlling, and LGBTQ+ people are rejected and discriminated against to the point of depression and isolation so severe that they see no alternative but ending their own lives. No, that is not a God I worship. That God is abusive. That God was an illusion created to represent the interests of an institution.

I'm so grateful I don't believe in that God anymore. No God that is loving would want me to experience that kind of shame. If God is love, there is nothing I need to do to prove myself worthy of it. In fact, the only thing that disconnects me from feeling God or Divine Love now is shame itself. Shame doesn't come from God. It's an emotion, an energy frequency, a state I experience within myself. You know what the solution is that brings me back to God? Compassion. Self-love. Opening myself to receive help and support from God when I'm suffering. The divinity and love I have inside reminds me God lives within me. That is where I find relief. You know where that love comes from? My feminine AND my masculine, often working together in sacred union depending on what I need. My feminine gives me the ability to soften, surrender, intuit, express, rest, release, and receive. My masculine helps me take aligned actions, be purpose-driven, tenacious, goal-oriented, set boundaries, and protect my vulnerability.

God is non-binary. Yes, it consists of feminine and masculine and includes polarity, but it's also as expansive, mysterious, powerful, dynamic, and limitless as unconditional love itself. God is love. Which means it's one thing and everything.

As I have been redefining my spirituality, I've been discovering truth buried beneath the things I was taught and the way they were taught. The language, packaging, and suggested interpretations don't resonate, but many of the concepts do. I've come to the conclusion that no religion has a monopoly on God or truth. It can be found anywhere, reaching all corners of the world, sometimes in the most unlikely of places. I can now more readily accept that goodness can come from the context of religion, from good-hearted people doing their best to live a good life. There are beautiful values of service, family, integrity, and compassion that can form a solid foundation to a great life. When people come together like that, there is something special that can happen in those communities. Spiritually connected people create beautiful things. Religion often attracts spiritually connected people who have good intentions and a desire to live with integrity. I believe I was one of those people who grew up with an innocent heart, seeking to build a connection with something larger than myself. I believe this is how I was able to have sacred, meaningful experiences despite also having painful experiences when I was active in the church. I know I was doing my best to live a good life based on what I was taught.

I also know I was struggling with an inner conflict that caused me to be judgmental, critical, and controlling of myself and others. This process has given me new insight to the meaning of "treat others how you would treat yourself." People's reactions are a reflection of themselves. I was judging others the way I was judging myself. As an adult, I understand that I get to choose what to believe, how to respond, and what to accept for myself. As I have worked through my healing, I've forgiven the people that perpetuate the harmful culture in the church. I still hold them accountable to do their work, but I also see it is a reflection of where they are. I used to be one of them.

I've forgiven myself for the judgmental, rigid, ignorant ways I projected my own discomfort onto others. I am still very capable of this, as I am still learning and growing. I do my best to make amends by setting my own boundaries, reclaiming my authenticity, and treating others with compassion, love, and acceptance. I will always be an advocate for self-love and acceptance to build a more tolerant and loving world. I will use my power of choice to respond to situations of injustice and choose to love people where they are with firm boundaries. Sometimes love looks like telling the truth and being bold enough to speak it when it may not be well-received or is not a popular opinion. Sometimes it means advocating for justice and using our own experiences to help make the world a more beautiful place or being a compassionate mirror and inviting someone to take accountability for their actions. Meeting judgment and shame with more judgment and shame seems like a formula for more social division and pain. Underneath all of the bullshit conditioning, most people want and need the same things and are doing the best that they can.

I have no interest in bashing the spiritual values or beliefs of others, including those in the religion I was raised in. My interest is in helping people recognize harmful aspects of a system and culture that get perpetuated by people. Meaningful change is only possible when we all do our part. I can have compassion *and* zero tolerance for behavior and choices that cause harm. I can point out when something is abusive and still believe in the possibility of change.

A major piece of this work is separating spiritual principles and concepts from the institution itself. Members of the religion are not at fault for being taught distorted versions of spiritual concepts in the form of dogma. The culture largely stems from the institution as a dysfunctional system. It is not simply a few members who have misunderstood, misinterpreted, or misapplied principles that are taught. The institution itself is flawed as it teaches principles for its own interest with an inability to be questioned. There is an authority structure and power dynamic that creates a toxic environment. The interest of the institution is for its leaders to be sustained as having "priesthood authority" or power to act and speak on God's behalf. Anything that challenges the integrity of the leaders or the teachings that come through them "from God" is deemed worthy of excommunication. This puts the power and authority of the leadership above the individual experience of its members and conflicts with the original intention of connecting people to God above all else. When people are raised in that environment, they are conditioned to respect authority and grow up believing that the church is infallible because its leaders are chosen by God as literal mouthpieces. This creates a dependency on the institution and leaders for spiritual guidance. It disconnects individuals from trusting themselves or cultivating their own direct relationship with God, personal revelation, discernment, and spiritual gifts.

Despite its shortcomings, I've come to realize that church can be a place for people to authentically connect with a higher power. It has a unique framework and definitions, but I think the individual spiritual experiences are genuine. The conditioned interpretations can be problematic because it puts spirituality in a box and creates confusion that is damaging anytime someone encounters cognitive dissonance with the doctrine. That confusion can disconnect people from authentic spirituality and create fear-driven patterns vs. true faith or intuition-based patterns. If they don't fit in the small box, it can be very hard to reconcile personally and socially. It creates a wedge between who they are taught they should be and a version of spirituality or higher power that fits authentically. One of the

28

greatest injuries this confusion can create causes people to doubt themselves and their ability to trust their own discernment. They are taught to doubt their doubts, and if they don't align with the one true church, its doctrine, and its leaders, there must be something wrong with *them*. They must be broken, inadequate, or unworthy.

The structure of institutional religion is what I find fault in because it causes harm and creates wounds that perpetuate a toxic culture. Individuals are taught to question themselves before they question authority or the system. This leads to indoctrination of shameful narratives and the pain of those wounds gets projected onto others through judgment, criticism, competition, comparison, exclusion, and rejection. God is not a religion or institution. Individuals can connect to God on a personal level anytime, anywhere. I believe churches should serve as places for people to gather and feel connected to themselves, each other, and God.

My definition of spiritual community is communing with God in unity with others, not to be confused with conformity or being the same. The key to this being effective is each person having sovereignty with personal connection to themselves and God, then cultivating a connection with others through a combination of witnessing and being seen. It involves a balance of love and support being given and received. If sovereignty and personal accountability were the foundation of spiritual communities, each person would be empowered with the tools to take what fits and leave what doesn't for their own path.

In my faith crisis, grief was a massive part of the process. I was grieving the familiarity and the feeling of certainty that came with what I had known. I felt a loss of spiritual connection in my confusion, a loss of security in my uncertainty, a loss of direction in my search for meaning, a loss of trust in authority in my experience of betrayal, and a loss of faith in God in the midst of my suffering. I have been surprised and relieved at how many spiritual concepts I have recovered from my childhood after disentangling them from the institutional definition. Was my grief necessary? Or was it needless suffering to lose what I had known?

No, it was not needless suffering. I had to lose what was to create space for what is—a more authentic, beautiful, expansive spirituality that fits me. It is a redefined version of principles in the spiritual realm, free of the confines, boxes, distortions, and limitations I experienced in religion. I am my own voice of authority and define my own truth. I discern tools that connect me to the Divine and bring me joy when I practice them.

Religion still doesn't feel like a safe spiritual home to me. I have my guard up because I have to. I have to sift through the bullshit to find the truth. Since I left the church, that's still been true as the world is also filled with bullshit and other people trying to tell me what to do. But now that I've built my spiritual home inside of myself, it's much easier. I can visit religious paradigms and excavate principles that resonate or integrate various perspectives from many different cultures to create my own collage of truth. I've concluded it doesn't matter how people connect to their spirituality, I just hope that they do in a way that is not oppressive, judgmental, or harmful to others. Diversity is part of what makes life beautiful. I want to celebrate the many colors, paths, experiences, and truths of others. I believe we can learn so much from witnessing and sharing with each other. It can operate like abundance, with an invitation to share, "Here's something that brings me joy... what do you think?" What if we treated it like an exchange of wisdom and every person has something valuable to offer from their own perspective? How different would our culture be?

I had a profound experience on Thanksgiving in 2020. I was driving home from my parents' house and was contemplating a question as I reflected on life's experiences. "What is the point of suffering? When we have negative or painful experiences, what is the purpose?" In a meditation that night, the answer came to me clearly and intensely. The point of life is to experience unconditional love. Suffering brings expansion, learning, and evolution to become One with God. I felt this truth and the phrase "God is love" in such a profound way it makes me tear up to this day. Every experience I have ever had has come with a lesson in love. Each time, I have learned another dimension of love for self, for others, and for life. This has brought me to believe that every experience is happening for me.

I know this concept is hard to accept as truth for many people because of the terrible things that happen in the world. Why do bad things happen to good people? How could there possibly be value in the darkness? There are certainly dark forces that exist and cause harm. Suffering is an inevitable part of life, a learning tool and byproduct of free agency to make choices with consequences. God, or Divine Love, is the constant that makes it all possible to transmute anything into strength. Diamonds are created with pressure. In my experience, the worst things that happened to me, or my greatest pain points, have become my greatest sources of strength. Anytime I have experienced resistance from the world, I gain resilience and wisdom that I would have never obtained otherwise. The discomfort of shame, oppression, and being raised in an abusive institution drove me to address big questions and issues inside myself. Had it not been for my devastating existential faith crisis, I would not be where I am. I am so incredibly grateful for where I am, who I am, and the expansion that has come from my suffering.

One of the most difficult practices has been learning to look for the gifts and lessons in each experience. I used to trip over the idea that when bad things happened to me it was because I must have *deserved* them. As though they were punishment for my sinful ways or for mistakes I had made. How different my perception has been since adopting the belief that life is happening for me. Even when I don't have clarity in the moment, I trust that it will become clear to me. I choose to believe that any discomfort I experience is happening to serve me in some way. I view life as a mirror that brings me experiences that reflect something for me to see or learn from.

One example of something that wasn't always clear how it could end up serving me was losing myself. From a young age, I self-abandoned to conform to the expectations I was given. I was deeply entrenched in perfectionism and people-pleasing to keep the peace and earn external validation. Much of this was adaptive and helped me survive the environment I was raised in. While my environment wasn't my fault and my adaptive strategies were part of my strength and resilience, these patterns were not sustainable and became painful, unfulfilling, and harmful to people around me. I'm grateful for the lessons those patterns taught me. Being disconnected from my inner voice only strengthened my resolve and clarity when I found it again. I needed the discomfort to overcome patterns of avoiding the inner child healing that I needed to face. Some of my wounds were buried in my subconscious until my shadows presented them to me. The painful patterns I was carrying and the unconscious strategies I was using for my unmet needs were no longer adaptive as I got older. They were no longer serving me. I needed to experience the stories I was carrying, reflected back to me by my life experiences, showing me where I needed healing. This led me to the concept of radical responsibility as a tool for regaining personal power by taking personal accountability. When I use the lens that life is reflecting what I need to see in myself, every experience presents an opportunity.

Looking back at my childhood, when the initial wounds were being created, it was difficult to see how there could be gifts in those experiences. I had done nothing to deserve them. Yet, I see the value in the lessons of unconditional love that have come from my own process of reparenting, forgiving my parents for their shortcomings, giving grace for their humanity, and gaining the ability to see and feel things clearly. I can now see beyond the incredible discomfort of being such a sensitive child who was tender-hearted, overly trusting, and naïve in a world that was not conducive to what I believed it could be. I don't say this cynically, though I certainly can have the proclivity to use cynicism for catharsis or emotional release. Instead, I see that my sensitivity was a gift in being able to see toxic things for what they were. It was heartbreaking.

My heart has always known what is possible and what can be created. My heart has always known how to love and how to be sensitive, forgiving, trusting, open, kind, curious, and joyful. Through my suffering, I have gained tools that help me protect my vulnerability, not suppress it. I have gained wisdom that helps me navigate the world and cultivate change that creates more inclusivity for kids like me. I have built a career devoted to inner child healing, to coming back to the nature of our hearts, our bodies, ourselves, our spirituality, nature, and each other. Vulnerability is the key to authenticity and connection. Every experience I've had that was harsh and unloving has taught me how to love even more broadly, strongly, and sustainably. Through these experiences, I learned to love myself with boundaries, self-acceptance, nurturing, and play. I affirm my tender heart by practicing vulnerability, allowing myself to express and be seen, and forgiving myself for mistakes I make. I am able to love others more effectively when I am able to love myself, take accountability, and recognize we are all the same at the core. We are not different or separate from each other. When I can see people are doing their best with their own growth edges, limitations, mistakes, and pain, it's easier to love them. When I set boundaries, it's easier to love others unconditionally. Boundaries are tools that allow love to expand. When love is at the root of everything, suddenly everything makes more sense. All of my emotions have purpose, all of my experiences have meaning, and I am able to see the beauty in everything.

As I have tried to explore my spirituality again, I can recognize parts that felt authentic and real from the past. I've always been a spiritual being. I have always had a relationship with the divine, and have always been a part of it. I was introduced to that connection through the lens of religion as *a* way, but not *the* most effective way for me and my journey. My soul knew that and ventured out to seek expansion of life and consciousness. I went through a profound loss and grieved as I shed layers of my identity and lenses that had given me a false sense of security in my youth. Lenses that were warped and tainted by voices of authority that weren't my own. My foundation was shattered and I've had to sift through the pieces of what was mine and what was given to me. This process has been difficult. I have wrestled with confusion and doubt, fear and anger, sadness and betrayal. I have learned to discern truth and trust my intuition. Anything that creates confusion or shame is not truth. These are signs of distortion. Full truth contains love, compassion, understanding, and clarity.

I am learning to trust the wisdom of my body in unison with my intuitive soul. I've been open, seeking, reaching, and embracing new experiences with the Divine that align with my heart and bring me peace and joy. I have discovered a true love for myself and have created a safe, stable, and supportive home within myself and in my body. Today, I see myself as powerful, confident, capable, passionate, driven, beautiful, compassionate, wise, and spiritual. I can stand in my body and trust the wisdom it holds. I can show love to my body and soul by nourishing, strengthening, and honoring what it needs. I can align my body and soul to flow harmoniously together and release what no longer serves me.

REINTEGRATING
THE DIVINE FEMININE

After my faith crisis, the sources I trusted most at first were the ones I could sense the most literally in my body. Things like nature, art, or meditation. I couldn't use the word "God" for a very long time because I didn't know how to relate to it in a safe way. I used words like "universe," "nature," or "source" to describe energies larger than myself. I had really beautiful experiences that remain sacred to me to this day. I can't describe the power in claiming my truth in my body, but I feel deeply and authentically connected to the natural world around me. My sensuality undeniably remains the most potent, powerful discernment method for recognizing truth and light.

Meditation has been essential in training my mind to work in collaboration with my body by giving presence, awareness, and conscious observation of the sensations in my body rather than remaining stuck in thought webs of endless analysis and solving unanswerable questions. Yoga was a powerful practice that allowed me to exercise these muscles of connecting my mindful presence, breath, and movement in my body. I was able to explore my emotions and feel them shifting with my movements. I was able to observe my entire state of being changing. I was also able to add intentions to my practice, almost like an embodied prayer. This was the path that led me to realize how powerful freedom of embodied expression can be. In combination with mindful breathing, yoga alleviated the stiffness I was carrying, giving my body permission to move more freely.

Society places many inhibitions on our ability to move and express freely like fear of judgment and how we'll be perceived. Once I found a way to give permission to my body in a space that felt safe, I liberated my joy in dancing! Not a choreographed or structured dance, just moving with presence and feeling. I began embodying my feelings as a way of transmuting them. Anywhere I felt tension, I would notice it and breathe, then explore movements in my body that came intuitively. I began to follow my pleasure and the movements that brought more joy, play, creative inspiration, and relief. I felt heaviness and tension leave my body. It wasn't long before I discovered I can experience a similar feeling when I sing. Permission was huge to unlocking my sacral chakra and setting my creativity free. These were the undeniable truths through corrective experiences that allowed me to connect with and befriend my body through my sensuality.

I discovered a tool that amplified this process exponentially, making me feel deeply seen. It was a method developed by Julianne Hough called Kinrgy. Her method combines breathwork, movement, and imagery with an emphasis on unique expression of the movements. This was a game changer for me. I had learned to embody the feelings I was already experiencing, but this practice helped me see how I could *create* a state of being through visualization and mental imagery paired with embodied movement, breath, and intention setting.

Finally, I began understanding the concept of manifesting! I was *playing* with the process of *creating* my life day by day, dance by dance. The same principles apply when visualizing something I desire for my life. I get clear on the image, the feeling, and the action that calls it into my being. I couldn't believe this power was right inside of me, by design, through the divine principles of creativity! All hidden within my sensuality, my sacral chakra, my womb space, my body. Of course! It had been right in front of me. Is that not where our bodies bring babies to life? Why not our dreams? It makes so much sense that creativity was linked to sensuality. It is something I had been disconnected from due to all the shame that cut me off from my body. Well, not completely. If this is what was possible through the pleasure of dance and breath, what was possible with the power of sex? Oh man, the shame that was wrapped around that one.

It made sense that I reconnected to my spirituality through divine gifts of my feminine essence. I had just left a religion that was so embedded with toxic masculine culture, the Divine Feminine was where I felt the safest. Many people who go through a faith crisis experience some degree of a pendulum swing as they find balance through the loss and explore their autonomy. It's like going through adolescence all over again. I have found value in the pendulum swing, as I am not able to feel whole or balanced without awareness of all sides of things. It was healing to connect with my feminine strengths, gifts, and way of being. The only way I had previously permitted myself to express my sexuality was through rebellious episodes of "acting out," indulging in what my body, nervous system, heart, and soul were demanding. The tragedy was I grew up resenting that aspect of my personality. Why was I so emotional? So sensitive? So passionate in love and so sexually driven? I didn't realize I had been rejecting manifestations of my Divine Feminine in a culture that was very effective at suppressing them.

Healing my spiritual wounds and defining an authentic identity started with healing my relationship to my feminine and the Divine Feminine/Mother that had been severely underrepresented in my childhood. As a little girl, I was taught many things about my role as a woman and what that means. Everything was gendered and segregated into clearly defined categories. Boys did boy things and girls did girl things. This was always confusing and frustrating to me, as I was a tomboy from a young age with a tenacity and inner strength that could take on anything that was presented to me. I wanted to do everything the boys were allowed to do and I wanted to exercise my strength. I played tackle football at recess, wrestled with all of my brothers, and have been athletic for as long as I can remember. In church activities, the boys got to do all the fun things while I was learning homemaking. I would have much rather been out camping, backpacking, repelling, canoeing, boating, whittling, shooting, ax throwing, and learning survival skills like building fires, foraging, or building things. It's not that I didn't enjoy some of the homemaking skills or find value in sewing, cooking, child-rearing, caregiving, and crafting. I simply resented that I wasn't included in the full spectrum of activities. I was never going to be the type of woman the culture was trying to shape me into being.

There were many unfortunate pieces to this. First, I felt like something might be wrong with me for being so different. Could I be feminine and also enjoy the athletic, outdoorsy things? Did that make me less of a woman or less desirable? I was confused by the mixed messaging on these topics in not just the church but in society. Another byproduct was that I rejected my femininity because I perceived it as weak. There was so much more to me than the socially acceptable categories. Men were the leaders, the spiritual teachers, and the empowered decision makers. I was disgusted by the idea of devoting my life in service of a man as his "helpmeet". As if I were not a whole, capable, independent, intelligent, spiritually connected being. This led to another pendulum swing and I compensated by cultivating my inner masculine.

I'm grateful for this swing because it is a massive part of who I am now, and what brought me here. It is part of my inner fire, my tenacity, my grit, my ambition, my leadership, my determination, independence, intelligence, advocacy, and purpose-driven nature. While I am grateful for the masculine that served me in many ways, I became easily exhausted and frustrated in my hyper-independence. Burnout was much more prevalent when I was not balancing it with softness and the ability to receive, surrender, slow down, rest, nurture myself, and create and appreciate life's beauty. I didn't know how to embrace pleasure, soothe my senses, and tune in to my intuition or the wisdom of my feelings. I didn't know how to access all of the embedded gifts in my body. Even when I did, I didn't know how to embrace and exercise them fully. I was resentful of my emotionality, my sensitivity, and my softness that suggested I was less capable of certain things than a man. I had internalized the cultural view of aspects that belong to the feminine.

There were mixed messages I was getting from the lessons taught about differences between men and women. On one hand, I was taught women were to be protected, respected, cherished, and honored in their feminine nature. On the other hand, only certain aspects of the feminine expression were accepted and celebrated. And it always came paired with an indication of "less than." Perhaps this message was more subtle and covert in the actions of how I saw women being treated. I've since learned that a sign of manipulation is inconsistency between words and actions. Women are not celebrated in the church (or in many aspects of society), and they are not cherished. It may appear so at times when they fit the mold of what is socially accepted, like the mother with numerous children who is modest, self-sacrificing, serving endlessly, caregiving, compassionate, meek, humble, mild-mannered, polite, devoted to her husband and her family, and obedient to her husband (the priesthood holder) and church leadership. They are not recognized for the fullness of their spiritual gifts, leadership, vision, creativity, expression, or sensitivity.

As I have begun integrating the wisdom of the Divine Feminine back into my authentic identity, I have discovered the wisdom and gifts She brings. She has taught me how to think less and feel more. Don't explain—express. Don't do, but be in truth. There is power in pleasure and beauty for the sake of beauty. There is no need to try to create when art is made through authentic expression. Being in the truth of our experience and allowing ourselves and our vulnerability to be seen is beautiful and priceless. Each expression is valuable and unique. That is part of the beauty; it's in being present and witnessing the experience of life in all its forms. There is no right or wrong, simply what is true in each moment. This naturally leads to connection, love, compassion, and abundance. Beauty is the law of attraction, just as it is. We attract what we are.

She exemplifies devotion to being one with love through giving and receiving. There is no chasing, grinding, or producing, but rather inviting, magnetizing, and creating with the love of Her being. She is the source of creation itself. I've also redefined concepts that I previously didn't understand about the Divine Feminine. There is a strength, resilience, ferocity, wildness, and unapologetic nature to it. Expression of truth is not always conventionally pretty, but it is beautiful.

I have found balance as I have embraced all dimensions of my personality and allowed myself to evolve into a multidimensional being. During my faith crisis, the pendulum swung away from the toxic masculine patriarchy to the safety of the Divine Feminine, getting back to nature and learning to trust myself and my intuition. It allowed me to open my heart again spiritually after the spiritual abuse I had endured and discover what was possible. With the foundation I built with the Divine Feminine, I was able to heal my relationship with the Divine Masculine. It was through integrating both that I reconnected to Divine Love and found balance within myself, my relationships, and my life. I'm so grateful I didn't give up on spirituality or allow the church I was raised in to define my spiritual identity. Having gone through this experience, I have now had the pleasure of supporting others on their journey to discover authentic spirituality for themselves and heal from spiritual wounds they have experienced.

One of the most rewarding aspects of this journey has been the connections I have made with other women. Healing my spiritual connection to the Divine Feminine brought depth and beauty to my relationships with women in a way I never thought would be possible. I feel inspired by the strength and wisdom of the feminine, as well as women who have done the work to heal their feminine and masculine aspects as whole, integrated, empowered beings. As we build each other up, we are not alone, and we are strong enough to heal the world, fill it with light, beauty, and pleasure, and reclaim everything that has always been ours. In collaboration with the Divine, we can become creators of our own universe.

I now use the terms "God" and "The Divine" interchangeably, which you'll notice throughout this book. I have a slight preference for The Divine, because it incorporates a concept more expansive and inclusive than the male-dominated religious depiction of God and all that comes with it. The Divine includes the Feminine, Masculine, and a host of spiritual energies that exist in the universe. I resonate with the concept of angels, spirit guides, ascended masters, and symbols from various traditions and religions that offer tools for unconditional love and healing. I choose to be devoted to unconditional love and work with light energies that operate in service of the highest good for me and for all beings. I use intuition and discernment to set boundaries and choose which spiritual energies I am open to channeling or communing with.

HIDDEN TRUTHS

Many concepts that I was taught when I was a child have been confusing to me because, in theory, they sound good and they seem true, but they caused a lot of pain and shame. I've realized this is a tool used by people or systems who are abusing their power and position of authority by distorting truth to fit their own priorities. I was being taught true principles, but in a distorted way through a lens of oppressive manipulation from a corrupt patriarchal system. Sometimes I use the word corrupt interchangeably with "shadowy." I'd like to hold institutions accountable for the impact of the philosophies and traditions that cause harm, but I also have to realize that institutions and systems are sustained by groups of individual people. When I discuss shadows, I realize people are not always aware of their shadows. We don't know what we don't know. But that doesn't make us less accountable to do the work to stop the harm and start to heal. We are still responsible for our impact and becoming aware of the ways we cause harm.

There comes a point that we all become accountable for upholding systems that cause harm and do not serve us, our children, and vulnerable members of our society, including minority groups and those affected by inequality. We are culture, which means we can also change it. This message doesn't have to be paired with shame, moral judgment, or blame. It is much more empowering to take accountability and ownership of the things that I am responsible for, have control over, and have the ability to change. I will never have it all figured out or run out of shadows to learn from and keep in check. I will spend my entire life learning about myself and how I can relate to the world around me with integrity. Life is a process of constantly evolving.

So, for systemic cultural issues like religion and sexuality, I don't envision a group of people sitting around a table scheming and plotting the demise of society as a whole. I do, however, see drastic inequalities and groups of people with more power, resources, and influence than others. I see vulnerable populations that are exploited by the inequality, power discrepancy, and lack of integrity within leadership. I see leaders abusing their power and exhibiting shadows such as greed, control, manipulation, and exploitation. I hold the leaders of institutions more accountable than the individual members because their actions hold more weight and create more impact, which comes with greater responsibility. Part of this responsibility is to be aware of the corrupt aspects of their institution, exemplify values to lead with integrity and personal accountability, and use their influence and power to minimize the harmful impacts of their institution both for its members and for humanity.

Some might say this view is idealist, as it's impossible to please everyone and effective leaders don't shy away from the thought of offending someone. I'd like to be clear, the harm I am speaking of is not hurting someone's feelings. I am speaking of the form of leadership corruption that seeks power over others, knowingly benefits from the suffering of others without taking any action to rectify it, and neglects accountability for the impact of their choices. The best way I know how to hold people in leadership positions accountable is by giving my support to leaders who embody the values in my heart. This starts with embracing the leader within me and working to become the leader I would like to see; to speak truth in the face of deceit, see inequality and the ways I benefit from the suffering of others, be invested in alleviating the suffering of others, seek power within myself through personal accountability and sovereignty, exercise my power with integrity, practice humility, stay open to learning with curiosity, share my vulnerability as a sign of strength and willingness to grow, value collaboration, and empower others in their own self-leadership.

As a spiritual leader, there is a duty to support others in cultivating their own personal relationship with the Divine and accessing their own spiritual gifts of discernment and intuition. This has not been my experience of most religious leadership. Not only is religion not the most effective environment for my own spiritual growth, but I have also seen the harm it has caused for so many. I can't support an institution or its leaders that are unwilling to take accountability for the suffering it causes and take strides toward meaningful changes. If I am embracing my own self-leadership and I can't create change in a system that is dysfunctional, it is my responsibility to remove myself from the system and live by my own set of truths. As a sovereign being, I get to discern what to keep and what to replace. As I've discussed in previous sections, many of the spiritual concepts did have value and truth to them. When I practiced them, I did experience beauty and light in my life. The problem was the distorted lens they were taught through, the religious dogma they were intertwined with, and the skewed interpretations I was indoctrinated with. This section is dedicated to concepts I have reclaimed and redefined as truths that were hidden in plain sight.

My body is a temple. This principle was taught to me through a lens of purity culture, modesty, body shame, and sexual repression. There were double standards and hypocrisies in what was deemed good and bad for the mind and body to keep it spiritually "pure" and "clean." This applied to media, food, clothes, friends, philosophies, language, lifestyle habits, and sexual practices. Since reclaiming this principle, I have a much more open definition of my body as a temple. I define a temple as a place dedicated to commune with the Divine. My body is a vessel that contains my consciousness, or the divine life force energy and love that exists within me. As I nourish and care for my body, mind, and energy, I become more sensitive, balanced, and aligned with my own divine being. I view sensuality as a divine gift that is part of my body's design and a tool for healing, discerning truth, and communicating with the Divine. The more aligned I am with my own divinity, the more connected I feel to God and the Divine energies beyond me. Embodiment is communion with the Divine. Conscious movement, breath, chanting, singing, prayer, lovemaking, pleasure, connecting with nature, and nurturing touch are just a few examples of ways to commune with the Divine. I can't think of a more powerful way to celebrate what it means to be alive as a spiritual being having a human experience.

Sex is sacred. This is another principle that was taught through the lens of purity culture. This message was paired with a specific interpretation and criteria that were considered acceptable for treating sex as sacred. Specifically, for sex to remain sacred, it was meant to only be shared between a man and a woman in the context of marriage. In some religious contexts, it has also only been considered appropriate for the purpose of procreation and doing it for the sake of pleasure is seen as taboo. The practice of solo sex is out of the question and considered "defiling your body."

In reclaiming the principle of sexuality as sacred, I wondered how I might define "sacred" after removing the lens of purity culture and considering sexuality as a spiritual gift. I had to go back to the root definitions of the word, using personal discernment to determine if

I could use this language and restore its original meaning. I discovered the word sacred comes from the root word "sacer," meaning holy and consecrated to God. I was also curious about the root of the word sacral, used to describe the chakra in the lower abdomen that houses feminine sexual energy and creativity. I learned the word sacral is derived from the root word "sacrum," meaning holy bone.

As I reconnected with my sexuality, it heightened my sensitivity and I experienced a deeper love and respect for myself and my body. I became more attuned to my body, my energy, my sensuality, and my boundaries. Through my own experiences, I was able to define what feels right for me in honoring my own sexual energy, body, pleasure, and spiritual practices. Tantric philosophies offered beautiful practices for nurturing my sexual energy with sacred intention and building a loving relationship with my vagina, or "yoni," as my temple.

The term yoni resonated deeply with me as I learned about various traditions related to sacred sexuality and the yoni as a sacred temple and portal to the Divine Feminine. It was so refreshing to hear such a beautiful, affirming narrative about my body and sexuality that celebrates the gifts of creation, pleasure, and connection to the Divine! As I applied this philosophy to my solo sex practice, I grew closer to the Divine and I naturally became more selective with my sexual partners. I became more sensitive to the quality of connection I desired when I was sharing that energy with a lover and I was able to define my own desires, boundaries, and standards. I developed a deeper trust in my intuition, desires, pleasure, body, and personal inspiration as a way of collaborating with the Divine. My connection to my own practice also deepened the quality of the intimacy I was able to share with my sexual partners as my standards began to reflect the same level of respect and intentionality with my yoni. The most significant takeaway for me has been the ability to reclaim this sacred energy as my own and to nurture it in whatever way I choose.

God communicates with us through modern revelation. This principle was taught to me through the lens of a specific religious context and used to validate the credibility of its leaders. It was used as a tactic to reinforce a patriarchal structure of male leadership with a specific leader designated as a literal mouthpiece and direct link to God. Men were also the only ones who could hold significant leadership positions and use God's power to facilitate blessings, rituals, and ceremonies. There were many warnings about false prophets and "philosophies of men" that were weapons of the devil to cause confusion and derail faithful people from the truth of God. There was a great deal of fear-mongering paired with a reassurance that there would be safety in following the teachings of the church leader who had been personally chosen by God. There were also messages about personal revelation and teachings about praying for answers through our own inspiration, but ultimately there was a deeply ingrained message of distrust in personal discernment and encouragement to rely on the leadership for answers. As I have reclaimed this principle, I see the irony in the warnings about false prophets and confusion as a tool for disconnecting people from God. I have experienced incredible beauty as I have learned to trust myself again, tune into my body, and listen to my intuition for personal communion with God. The most significant distortion here has been relying on any other person or entity to define truth for me. I have a direct link to the Divine within myself through personal revelation and inspiration.

I am a child of God with a divine nature. This principle was taught to me in a very specific context with a very specific interpretation. There was a lot of detail in what it meant to be a child of God with heavenly parents (only one of which was ever discussed), and what the purpose of this life is. I was given a comprehensive narrative that answered all the questions of why I am here, where I came from, and where I am going after I die. Since reclaiming this principle, I have discovered my own authentic identity and purpose in life that I am passionate about. I have made meaning of my existence in a way that feels deeply important to me.

If God is love, and I am born of God, I am also love. When I embody pure love, I am One with God. There is an interconnectedness in all things and separation is an illusion. God is the Divine Masculine and the Divine Feminine. Just as I carry physical DNA from both of my parents, I have energetic traits of masculine and feminine, like divine DNA. The Divine is in everyone and everything, including me. I have a Divine nature that carries so much incredible wisdom in my being. I am a conscious spiritual being having an embodied experience, as an expanded way of enjoying life, marveling in the beauty of it, and being a part of it. There are infinite possibilities for expansion and creation within this lifetime and beyond. Being in alignment with truth is to embody creative energy, pleasure, joy, beauty, interconnectedness, and the full spectrum of emotionality. I am nature created by nature. All of the patterns around me in nature are mirrors for what I am. I am light and dark, creation and destruction, life and death, the five elements and energy chakras, with an energy body and a physical body.

JOURNAL PRACTICE:

1. What do these concepts mean to you? *The body is a temple. Sex is sacred. God communicates with us through modern revelation. Being a child of God with a divine nature.*

2. Have you found any principles that were taught to you through a distorted lens?

RADICAL
ACCEPTANCE

A cknowledging my insecurities and allowing myself to experience my deepest vulnerability, opening my heart to feel my suffering, has been the key to a liberated self. This is different from being consumed by the pain, building an identity around it, or wallowing in a victim mentality with disempowerment. Feeling these wounds and allowing the pain to be witnessed and expressed has been the most effective method for accepting my emotions, releasing them, and, perhaps the most significant piece, surrendering. Surrendering to receive, opening my heart, and asking the Divine to heal me. I allow the burden to be lifted from me with the help of my spiritual guides.

This may look different for each person. Some may identify with God, nature, source, Christ, Allah, a higher self, angels, Buddha, or other symbols and deities that represent the Divine. Personally, I feel God in everyone and everything. God is a non-binary, formless, shape-shifting energy of unconditional Love that takes whatever form is needed to meet me where I am. I most often feel it through Christ, the Divine Masculine, the Divine Mother, and a higher self that is wise and kind. I feel it when I dance, sing, journal, listen to music, or read poetry. I feel it in yoga, meditation, nature, and small synchronicities with perfect timing. I feel it in laughter with friends, my mother's hugs, a meal made with love, and intimate lovemaking. I see it in my solo sex practice, in my prayers, and in angels on earth and above that hold me through my tears. I see it in the patterns that make up my life, the full circle moments when everything makes sense. I see it in the miracles of this existence, the full spectrum of emotions, and the magic in connection. I see it in the medicines that offer relief, both eastern and western, and the experiences of my ancestors who have passed down their wisdom.

I can only speak to what has been true in my experience. I can't speak for all people and I am very aware that my life has been gifted with a lot of privilege. I've had access to opportunities and resources that have helped me heal and transmute my pain into something beautiful. I think it's important to acknowledge that. I also believe that there is something more universal than external factors. Some might describe it as a person's soul, life force energy, or consciousness—an inner strength and fire that fuels how a person responds to their circumstances. There are gaps in opportunities, education, and resources that affect each person's experience. There are also internal resources that nobody can give you or take from you. It is the essence of you. It is your personal power, your ability to choose what to do with what is given to you. It's the collective wisdom and strength of your ancestors that have been passed down to you. It's your mind, the beliefs that you accept as truth, the power of thought, and the ability to apply the knowledge and wisdom within you. It's how you can balance, access, and alter the energy field within and around you. It's internal self-mastery, your own inner divinity. In collaboration with the Divine, these are tools that allow you to discover an authentic identity and create a new reality.

We are never alone. It is impossible because we are all One. We are all connected to the same universal life force of energy. Our conscious perceptions are fabricated by our experiences and lack of experience, for we learn through experience and are constantly adapting and evolving our understanding of the world around us. My relationship with God is the best one I've ever been in. It is also my relationship with Self, my inner divinity. Relationships are a practice. Perfect relationships do not exist. Accepting all aspects of myself and integrating them with love is how I practice being in relationship with God. I embody unconditional love to the best of my ability and level of awareness, and I commit to being receptive to being opened more fully by Love. Each experience of Divine Love brings deeper understanding. The degree to which I am able to practice this within myself translates to my ability to practice unconditional love for others.

This relationship is a practice of trust and surrender, choosing to believe in the power of the universe to provide and be available as long as I am open to receiving it. The Divine Masculine is my provider—the container and structure providing consistent presence and support. The Divine Feminine is my muse—my intuition and inspiration for flow and creative expression. Together, these qualities create balance, a beautiful yin and yang of life. The masculine helps me to be proactive, to do, plan, move, execute, and go. The feminine helps me to be still, to listen, notice, feel, integrate, rest, create, express, and be. There is wisdom and strength in both. Listen. Tune in. Feel. Integrate. Rest. Move. Create. Express. Love. Be. Do. This is life, we are learning to live it with love and joy and fullness. What a gift it is to be present and embrace all aspects of ourselves with radical acceptance and unconditional love.

The parts of me that are the hardest to love need more love, not less. The ones I reject or struggle to accept are the parts of me that are wounded, the most uncomfortable to feel, the most destructive if I neglect, and the ones I need to embrace the most. They are the ones who hold hidden gifts and strengths on the other side of the pain. As

I heal and accept all parts of myself with unconditional love, I become whole and am more connected to my inner divinity and to God.

There is beauty and wisdom in the light and the dark, each with their own shadows and gifts. The light has truth that was represented in my religious upbringing, but it was cloaked in the shadow of purity culture with untruths that disconnected me from God. One of the greatest distortions I was taught is that my sexuality separates me from God, and that in my natural state, I am inherently sinful and unworthy. As I have recognized these shadows of the light side of spirituality, it has allowed me to restore the truth and innocence of myself as a divine sexual being, inherently worthy of love, pleasure, and joy. I am on a journey of learning and growing through this life experience to embody the truth of who I am and become one with love.

The dark was also represented in my upbringing, with the shadow of fear-based compliance and disempowerment that reinforced shame, created inner conflict, and condemned desires, fantasies, pleasure, and any expression that was seen as confrontational or socially deviant. Integrating these shadows has allowed me to reclaim my anger, passion, boundaries, pleasure, desire, freedom of expression, and self-acceptance. I now see the value and beauty in the darkness, in death, in burning down what doesn't serve, in setting boundaries, in claiming desires, and in loving the seemingly unlovable parts of me. I see that I need the dark and the light to be whole, balanced, happy, healthy, and free. Through my personal practice of radical acceptance, it has restored the truth of light and dark to the fullness of what they can be—in shadows causing harm or in service of healing.

PART TWO

SEXUALITY WITHIN

SACRED SEXUALITY:
HEALING AND INTEGRATING

I was surprised by how difficult this topic was to write about. I don't know why I was surprised; it's pretty obvious. But still, I was surprised how painful it was to remember just how much shame and confusion was wrapped around the topic of sexuality for most of my life, until very recently. It does make this celebration of where I am that much sweeter, giving myself credit for all that I've come through and endured to get here. I am nervous and excited to share the beauty, bliss, and joy of what I've discovered in my own sacred sexuality practice. It's easy for me to talk about with my friends, family, or strangers one-on-one. But allowing it to be seen on such a wide platform by people I have never met... that's terrifying.

Logically, it's all very clear to me. There's nothing to fear if all I'm doing is sharing my truth. It's a beautiful truth! It's precious to me. Who cares what other people think? And yet, I remember those feelings. The shame, the judgment, the story about being unworthy. It was so deeply ingrained in my social conditioning that it's hard to completely eliminate. I still have edges that come with flare-ups of shame when I run into them. The most honest thing I can say is, I've been there. I've been wrapped in the thick, black cords of sexual shame and repression, where the only things keeping me from

56

freedom were untruths I had been taught to believe. But I didn't realize the power within me.

I was so preoccupied with what I was told and I was trying to be obedient, righteous, and worthy for external figures of authority. I believed the toxic, distorted messages about my worth and body, pleasure and sensuality, purpose and destiny, and the very specific prescription to be worthy of God's love. I believed that my natural proclivity for seeking pleasure was sinful and unholy. As a young, impressionable child, what choice did I have but to accept what was taught to me so convincingly? I had no defenses. I was not equipped to discern truth for myself yet. I had been conditioned to depend on older, wiser, more powerful, and more spiritually connected men to tell me how to earn God's graces.

Many women view sexuality as an obligation or responsibility that comes with being in a relationship and creating a family. Other views of sexuality reduce it to a basic physical pleasure that is shallow, unsophisticated, uninspiring, or dirty. I believe sexuality can be a woman's direct channel to her spiritual gifts and connection with the Divine, and that sensual pleasure is every woman's birthright. Reclaiming the power of sacred sexuality can liberate women to a new level of connection to themselves, their bodies, their creativity, their intuition, their relationships, and a higher power, life purpose, and life satisfaction.

I understand why sexuality isn't a priority to many women. Why would it be when it has been male-dominated for so many centuries? Female pleasure has not been the main priority unless it's to meet a man's needs. It's been reinforced as a chore, a responsibility, and a "wifely duty." If you're in a relationship and you don't desire sex, the narrative is, "Well, it's an important aspect of a relationship, so you better fix it to keep your partner happy." Often, sexuality is not something women have enjoyed or viewed as a priority for themselves. Women, I see you. This process can be exhausting. Why would you have an interest in something that has never been allowed to be about you? It's been either to have babies, keep a man happy, feel like you have to perform, or prove you are enough and worthy, like all the women you are compared to. When sex is centered around men, it creates a culture of seeking love and external validation by subscribing to a standard of what is desirable to them. It teaches us to hate our bodies, conform to a social "norm," and compete with ourselves and each other to make men happy. It's fucked up, but it's true. We can get so distracted by coping with all of the distortions and bullshit we're inundated with that we have nothing left to give ourselves.

Ask yourself: What gives me pleasure? Am I even allowed to enjoy sexual things or does that make me slutty? Think about the differences in the way boys are raised when it comes to personal sexual identity, masturbation, sexual activity, desires, and familiarity with their own anatomy. For women especially, talking about it isn't okay, so it's wrapped in secrecy and shame.

What if it didn't have to be that way? What if you considered what sexuality could mean for you if it was just for you? What could it be if not in the context of your relationship? Do you have your own sexual identity? Is it one that is making you happy and allows you to live most authentically? If it feels overwhelming to think about, don't worry, you're not alone. From a young age, women are conditioned to repress their own sexuality through double standards, purity culture, and slut-shaming. The only thing men fear more than other men is a woman who is fully empowered. Why would she need him if she could meet her own needs? How else would he feel power and security? The new age of female sexuality is one of desire, not merely function or needs. It is one of choice, sovereignty, and authentic intimacy.

I know there are a million reasons exploring sexuality has been uncomfortable emotionally, physically, and spiritually. It's commonly something to be avoided or grown accustomed to living without. Why would you need it? Who has time for that? If it's not a priority to you, you have plenty of other things to do, and you've gone this long without it being a large part of your life. In fact, you may have been taught it made you more righteous or worthy to repress sexual urges with scripture verses like "the natural man is an enemy to God." Controlling your impulses is something to be celebrated, right? Maybe not. It is cutting you off from a major source of life force energy, spiritual connection, and some of the most precious gifts in the human experience–pleasure and creativity.

Motherhood is magical and nothing short of a miracle. Some traditions consider a woman's womb to be an interdimensional portal to the spiritual world. No matter what your spiritual views are, there is something marvelous about the creation of life. Growing a living being and birthing a human with their own consciousness into the world is all made possible through the power of sexuality and creation. It seems tragic that this power has often been limited by various cultures and religions to serve only one purpose in a single context when we have the ability to create so much more with our existence.

What if that same power could be used to bring other things to life? Is your only purpose to procreate and exist for others? What other dreams do you have inside? What if you could plant the seed, grow it, and birth it into reality? What would you use that sacred energy for? What kind of legacy do you want to leave? What if I told you your sexuality can be a portal to birthing your dreams and creating your own reality? I've met too many women who are exhausted, burnt out, touched out, and can't even stomach the idea of sex because it has never been for them. Or they pressure themselves to prioritize it to satisfy men and maintain stability in their relationships. When I ask them what's in it for them, they seem surprised by the question.

Some of the natural gifts of the feminine are to be nurturing and compassionate, which are often the aspects most emphasized in our culture. Culturally, women are often expected to be caretakers and selfless givers, while other aspects of the feminine get neglected or rejected. I believe this is why so many women get stuck in cycles of burnout and exhaustion. I also believe it's part of a feedback loop as both a cause and a result of the sexual repression of women. A fundamental characteristic of the Divine Feminine is to receive. When women allow themselves to consider that sex could be for their own pleasure and enjoyment, it might be shocking to them. For them to receive nurturing, pleasure, joy, creativity, and relief after all the giving.

What if we went back to the beginning and allowed ourselves to normalize sensuality and pleasure within our own bodies? What if it wasn't shameful, obligatory, or a responsibility? What if we could just appreciate the beautiful nature of our bodies and the pleasure they are capable of? What if it got to be something that is for you and actually promoted a deeper, more loving relationship to yourself and your spirituality? Would you be interested in that? What if your pleasure was not dirty, selfish, shallow, carnal, sinful, or slutty? What if, instead, it was up to you to explore and define its meaning? What truth might you discover? Which parts of you would you be reclaiming? Which narratives would you be exchanging?

Whether you are single or in a relationship, this work is available to you. Confront outdated, inaccurate, and oppressive patterns of control that keep you stuck and at war with yourself, and replace them with what you discover to be true. Just like anything else, when we identify a distorted thought or behavior pattern that does not serve us, we can take action to align with a higher truth. In this way, self-massage and solo sex practices can be a beautiful, conscious act of rebellion. I refuse to believe my pleasure is wrong, shameful, or something to avoid and hide. When I choose to touch myself with loving, radical acceptance, it is an act of rebellion against the messages I was conditioned to believe about my body, pleasure, worth, and spirituality. It rewires my brain to align with a more accurate sense of self.

There are other ways women allow themselves to indulge in sensuality–massages, spa days, fragrances or aromatherapy, dancing, yoga, luxurious clothing, baths, chocolate or other indulgent foods, beautiful flowers, music, time in nature, or hair and makeup routines that make them feel beautiful and give them time just for themselves. My wish is that women can feel free to reclaim sexuality as a way to love and nurture themselves, experience pleasure, express creativity, embody love, and cultivate a rich connection to self and others. I'd like to reverse the impacts of centuries of sexual repression, shame, and women's sexuality being oppressed and controlled by men. I hope to bring solo sex practices out of the shadows and replace the narrative that it is dirty, sinful, or shameful and restore it to the beautiful gift that it is.

There should be nothing wrong with a woman fully embodying her sensual essence. It is an absolutely beautiful thing to experience and celebrate. Sexuality is an entire realm of sensuality that is missed due to the taboo nature and toxic culture around it. Historically, men have felt insecure, intimidated, and threatened by empowered women. Somehow it became a competition of power, control, jealousy, and possession. On the other end of the spectrum, the idea of a woman pleasuring herself has been so fetishized as a result of being taboo that it has become something to serve the arousal of men too. This is part of the reason women who seek support with sexuality set goals to be more sexual for their partners, not for themselves. I'm not saying women being connected to their sexuality can't be arousing, sexy, fun, and pleasurable. I'm simply making the argument that for too long it has been *only* about men. Things are changing in this modern era of feminism, but there is a lot of reclamation work to do to balance out the effects of shame, oppression, and abusive dynamics around sex that have been passed down for generations.

Engaging in a solo sex practice allows a woman to really explore her edges, interests, pleasure, and connection to herself without the distractions, influence, preferences, and stimuli of another person. It's a powerful starting place for a woman to really discover herself and develop a sexual identity. Of course, this can also be explored in partnership with intention, safety, communication, connection, and boundaries. My objective is to highlight both contexts for women to explore their sexuality within and between, expanding their experience of pleasure for themselves as a spiritual practice, and with their lovers.

If you are a woman considering embarking on this journey and exploring your sexuality, congratulations. Choosing yourself is a huge first step and it takes courage to lean into a growth edge, especially one as uncomfortable as sexuality can be. I'm excited for what you will experience as you embrace your own exploration to redefine your sexual identity. You can expect to feel more connected to yourself, your body, your pleasure, and your sensuality. It can lead you to more beauty than you have ever known, and receive more love than you ever thought possible. You know how they say when you love yourself first, you're better able to love others? It's true. Moreover, when you give to yourself and allow yourself to receive, you're more able to take in love and support from others. This allows you to continue giving your gifts sustainably, with more balance and less burnout.

Life is meant to be enjoyed. There will always be hard things, but there should also be beauty, joy, pleasure, and creativity because it's all part of the human experience. It's the whole point of being embodied consciousness–to live fully and love the bodies we are in. You'll also find that this isn't just about sex, it's about upleveling the quality of your whole life. You may feel increased energy, creativity, passion, zest for life, health, connection, acceptance, peace, or joy. You'll have the power to create your own reality and fall in love with the life you're living. Pleasure truly is an expansion of what you already experience but might miss. If we do not allow ourselves to be open to all of it, we miss out on fully feeling joy in each precious moment.

You deserve love. You are worthy. You are beautiful, divine, and connected to life all around you. You are a part of nature and you have magic inside of you. You possess powerful gifts that can be an incredible source of healing, not only for you but for everyone. Healed people heal people. We are all interconnected. I have lived it. I have discovered my own magic and found love and beauty beyond my wildest dreams. My life is messy and very imperfect, and I'm absolutely in love with it. I want everyone to experience love for themselves the way I have finally learned how to. I want everyone to receive love and support from others and to have a connection to a higher power that is fulfilling, meaningful, and authentic to them.

Sexual and spiritual healing have been a massive part of my journey to get here. They have been major themes throughout my life and were once some of the most painful aspects of my experience, but are now my greatest sources of strength and joy. I still lose myself sometimes, temporarily, but I've also learned to recognize it and come home to myself. I've learned to come back into alignment and create a state of flow and juicy sensual joy within my own being. It's the most precious, beautiful gift to finally discover how to fill myself with so much love that it comes pouring out to everyone and everything.

The best part is, truth lives inside every woman. For some, it's buried deeper than others, beneath layers of untruths. But pleasure is in your nature; your body is designed to experience it. We naturally seek pleasure and comfort when we are children and, somehow, we forget or learn to repress those desires. We are taught to control ourselves–to become responsible. Why can't we be responsible and enjoy life to the fullest? Why does it have to be either/or? Can you remember what gives you joy and pleasure? What does your body like to experience? It already knows what to do, you just have to trust it. This wisdom is kept in the body; it's a part of nature passed down through your genes. We inherit many things from our ancestors, some good and some challenging. The capacity for sexual pleasure has existed from the beginning. It is the source of life. The creator of all things. Doesn't it make sense that sexuality is godly energy? It has great power with potential to cause great harm or incredible healing and beauty. Fearing it, repressing it, avoiding it, shaming it, or controlling it are all common ways to navigate this energy that lives in all of us. Is that really the best way to master it? What if we instead befriend and integrate it, learning how we can engage with it and allow it to enhance our experience?

The first step is removing all the shame from it. No more judgment, no more repression, no more denying our own nature, no more purity culture. Those things reinforce a narrative that something is inherently wrong with us. Let's empower ourselves with accurate information and honor the need for each individual to discover their own path with sexuality. It is a personal journey and there is no one-size fits all path. Let's reduce harm by taking the fear-mongering out of education in schools, religions, and homes and replace it with comprehensive education including health considerations, emotional preparedness, and pregnancy prevention. Let's teach children and adults about consent, boundaries, and options for outlets and forms of expression that are not harmful to themselves or others physically, mentally, emotionally, or spiritually. Let's encourage children and adults to have a positive relationship with their bodies and to be accountable for themselves and their actions. Trying to control others' choices is ineffective and does not promote accountability in yourself or them. Perhaps we need to develop a tolerance for people to make mistakes because it's necessary to learn by living.

We can restore truth in our bodies through our own exploration and honoring the wisdom of our intuition. We can allow our bodies to inform and guide us and embrace our pleasure as pure and innocent with curiosity and compassion. Connecting to suppressed desires has hidden gifts of embracing and loving our shadows and rewriting the internalized stories about ourselves. One example of this might be exploring the narratives around being a "good girl" vs. a "slut." It can be useful to observe the stories around things that have been labeled wrong or dirty and consider what we choose to believe based on our own experiences and inner knowing. This can be one of the gifts of embracing our fantasies, especially the ones we are afraid to explore, accept, or express. Eroticizing things that have been suppressed, shamed, or exiled within us is an opportunity to reclaim those parts of us. This is alchemy–taking something painful and turning it into pleasure and beauty.

WHERE TO BEGIN

As I embarked on my own healing journey and recognized the wounds I had around sexuality, I wasn't sure where to start. And then it dawned on me. Start at the beginning. Duh. My inner child was the most wounded–the one who never got what she needed, who needed me the most and yet was the most vulnerable and uncomfortable to acknowledge. After all, I had spent the majority of my life adapting to my environment, which meant abandoning her. Even worse, I had blamed her, resented her, and internalized the messages I had received about her... about me. Those patterns of perfectionism run really deep. So of course that's where I needed to go for my healing. That's where it all started–the messages and social conditioning about my body and sexuality. It's all connected, isn't it? How we feel about ourselves, our bodies, our pleasure, our desire, and our ability to receive. It all affects our capacity for joy, love, connection, creativity, power, and spirituality.

In my process of healing, I've become a witness to the younger me who experienced so many messages about beauty and body image and modesty. It was the last place I wanted to be, reliving things that were so painful to see. How could I help her? How could I teach her? I held on to the fact that I'm here now, and I finally have the ability to give her what she's always needed and deserved: to be seen, loved, accepted, and free. I have the power to protect her, set

the record straight, re-parent her, and introduce her to the Divine–
the loving kind. Best of all, I get to teach her about the Divine
Feminine, the balanced Divine Masculine, and how both exist
within me. I can play with her, nurture her, hold her, witness her
fears, comfort her, make it safe, and get support when I can't do it
alone. I collaborate with the Divine to set her free to follow her joy
and reclaim the innocence of her body. I spend time doing things
that feel good. I replace the "I don't knows" with my newfound
truths. I practice and expand on them. I open my heart to life and
love from the sources I have determined to be safe and trustworthy.

I used to feel so much shame for the rebellious ways of my teenage
years. My body was often in a trauma response and my nervous
system was so fried, it carried stress like a sponge. As a highly
sensitive person, I took in so much stimulation from everything and
everyone. I had to scream at the end of the school day just to get it
out. Or I'd strip completely naked to provide sensory deprivation
when my system was overheated. I always naturally gravitated
toward human connection. My nickname was "Julie Bug" when I
was young because I was such a cuddle bug. My body already knew
how to soothe and reset from stress. As a natural progression, that
translated into sex as I got older.

As a deep feeler, love was intense. My desire for connection and
safety was instinctual and teenage hormones were like lighter fuel.
My body spoke one language and knew what to do. The result was
a fierce tendency to become hypersexual. Not recklessly, but in the
culture I was raised in, it may as well have been, and I was labeled
a slut. It was an internal dilemma, feeling so strongly wired one way
from the core of my being, but conflicting with everything I was
taught to believe. Sex was wrong, sinful, unrighteous, and shameful,
especially at that age. It was to be controlled. That's how I was to
stay in good graces with God–to deny my carnal nature, the natural

man. What the fuck? God made man, but created them in a way that made them an enemy to themselves? To him? It didn't make sense but it must have been my humanity that didn't understand. At least that's what I told myself to dismiss my own questions.

So, I was left with this inner conflict–live my truth or make God proud and earn approval. What was a young, developing, insecure, perfectionist girl to do? Both, of course. Followed by soul crushing shame spiraling at the impossible paradox inside of me. Too much. Not enough. It was like sexual bulimia. Binge, shame, repent, restrict, repeat. Religious abstinence induced sexual bulimia. I'd get to a breaking point of control, exhausted by the perfectionism and stress of trying to have it all together all the time and trying to do everything right. I'd reach "fuck it" and allow myself to indulge in what I really wanted but thought was "bad" for me. It felt reckless and impulsive and yet it was completely normal and healthy behavior. My "acting out" was expressing love and affection and seeking connection and pleasure with partners I was in a relationship with.

The rebellion felt exhilarating and exciting, but the crash afterward was anguishing. Almost immediately after passionate lovemaking, I'd curl up in a ball and start sobbing from shame. I was such a disappointment, what was wrong with me? God must be so hurt; I couldn't possibly still be worthy. For my partners, how confusing it must have been. Could they trust my yes? Were they doing the right thing? Were they the cause of my suffering? Of course not. But how were they to know what to make of such drastic mood swings? If I could scoop myself up from those painful memories, I'd wrap my naked body in the coziest, fuzziest blanket, brush my hair away from my face, and kiss my forehead. I'd tell me exactly how opposite my fears were from the truth. I'd tell myself that the thing I was so worried was wrong with me was actually my greatest source of strength and a sign of my resilience. It would be the thing that helped me heal, and not just myself but so many others who have suffered too.

I'd tell myself how perfectly imperfect I was and how pure my heart and body are. How innocent I was in my sexual pleasure, and how beautiful it was that I could express my human nature. I'd tell myself how I didn't need to be afraid of losing God's love or being unworthy of blessings because of my sexuality. I'd tell myself how sexuality is a gift of life. It is a blessing and part of our design to experience pleasure, joy, healing, and relief from suffering. I'd tell myself all about my sacred magic that comes from sexual practice and how I've never felt closer to the Divine than when I'm deep in solo sex. I'd tell myself how my sexuality is one of my greatest sources of power. That people are only scared to talk about it because of their own shame. That lies have been passed down in our culture for generations and made people afraid. That it has never been true that we separate ourselves from God when we embrace our sexuality and embody our pleasure. I'd tell myself that nothing can change my worth. Nothing.

Healing has involved an integration of all parts of me. The child that should have felt free in her body. The adolescent that shouldn't have felt so much shame (or any) about her developing, natural, beautiful sexuality. She should have been supported through her first bleed as a rite of passage with opportunities for embodied rituals, honoring her sensitivity and awakening spiritual gifts to continue expanding her creativity. Children dream and play and create in their worlds of imagination. As they grow older, they gain power and abilities to bring these dreams into reality. They continue cultivating strengths that equip them for self-mastery and expansion in this life, if only given the tools, opportunity, and support to succeed in developing authentically who they are meant to be. And most importantly, determining for themselves who they want to be.

Healing sexuality is about giving my adolescent self a reformed, comprehensive sex education. Burning down the ineffective, shame-inducing, abstinence-only curriculum. We have to do better. She deserves to know the truth about her body, her beauty, her pleasure, and her power! What if we taught her about her anatomy and how to explore her own pleasure and sensuality? What if we taught her to connect her spirituality with her body and her pleasure as part of its beautiful design? What if we taught her how to embrace and feel through her big emotions, how to express and release them without judgment? What if we taught her how strong her vulnerability and sensitivity make her? That her ability to feel, love, and express are all gifts of the Divine Feminine that hold the keys of creation, manifesting, and compassionate leadership. That being connected to her body makes her a powerful visionary, intuitive, and more effective leader. That her confidence comes from embracing her body and her gifts, practicing radical acceptance, love, and compassion for all of herself. That when she loves herself, she is a better human and is a gift to the world just by being authentically who she is. That a part of self-love is loving touch and appreciation for all the body does. That pleasure is a service to the body. A way of giving back, nurturing it and celebrating this lifelong companionship and gift of being alive. That pleasure is a birthright and an essential natural medicine for balancing emotions, hormones, stress, and counteracting anxiety and depression. Do you realize how fucking different my adolescence would have been? Can you imagine what I could have spent my entire 20s doing instead of healing?

It's okay. The anger is justified. It's righteous indignation and repulsion for the injustice of the control and oppression of all women. There is so much injustice in so many categories, it would be exhausting to list. The ripple effects of this oppression are extensive and well-covered in other books. But it's important to feel that–to acknowledge the loss, grief, and rage. She deserved better. We all do. We can't change what's already happened but we can decide to fight now and make it right for ourselves, our sisters, and our children.

If you are in a position of privilege, remember that where much is given, much is required. We need you. It's your choice to decide what to stand for, so consider this a formal invitation–no matter what your background, political interest, ethnicity, anatomy, or scope of influence, join me in making it right by starting with you. With your inner child. Ask the hard questions, let her be seen. Witness her experience. What did she really need? When society was busy trying to "protect" her by scaring and shaming her away from her body, obsessed with preventing her from embracing her sexuality for the socially constructed concept of purity (a mechanism established for control and manipulation of women by men), tell me, what was she feeling?

Don't take it from me. These answers can only be found inside of you. You are your own voice of authority, the keeper of your wisdom, the writer of your story. When it comes to sexuality, what were you taught, or not taught? What did you, or do you, believe? What is your relationship like with your body? How do you feel about pleasure? How well do you know your own anatomy? Have you seen it, touched it, gotten to know it? How do you feel about your genitals? What gives you pleasure? Not just sexual arousal, but sensual enjoyment in your body. What questions do you have that you never had an opportunity to ask? What do you wish you had been taught about your body? About sexuality? About pleasure?

I DIDN'T KNOW
WHAT I DIDN'T KNOW

I once learned that sexuality was something that had to fit in boxes to be acceptable. Outside those boxes I'd be shunned from God's presence and my sin would be treated akin to murder in severity. If I explored beyond those boxes, I would be unworthy and die spiritually. Interesting that the boxes were actually what suffocated me and almost killed my authentic desire to deepen spiritually. If religion was the only way, I wanted nothing to do with it. It hurt me, manipulated me, and exploited my open-hearted curiosity to use it against me. To gain control, loyalty, submission, and money, draining my true spiritual gifts and sucking up my life force energy. I was furious when I discovered I'd been deceived and convinced as a child to blindly believe what this authority told me, as though I didn't have the capacity to commune with the Divine myself. It created a wound so deep I almost closed off entirely, unwilling to be trusting of anyone or anything. This chapter came from my own reflection of my inner teen and how different things would have been if I had been taught differently.

I didn't know. When I was a little girl, I didn't know that it was normal for me to be curious about my body, to explore my sexuality at a developmental level–touching and looking at my anatomy, playing doctor with the neighbor girl with mutual curiosity, and that we weren't doing anything wrong or dirty. I didn't know I didn't need to be ashamed of my natural way of being–that feeling pleasure from touching myself was a normal and healthy thing. I didn't know that my body was perfect the way it was, with all of its uniqueness, and it didn't have to look like anyone else's to be worthy of love, to be beautiful, or to be accepted. I didn't know that it didn't matter what I wore on my body, how I dressed, how much skin was showing, or where I was–there was nothing inappropriate. That no social construct can change the truth of my innocence, my nature, and my being. I didn't know that I was unconditionally loved by God, the Divine, the universe, life itself. I didn't know that when I was told I needed to dress modestly for other people's thoughts, that was never my responsibility. That when someone else acted outside of integrity, it was a reflection of them and had nothing to do with me. I didn't know that when I was molested as a child, it was very wrong of him and he needed to take accountability. I didn't know that forgiveness was something I got to choose for my own healing in my own timing, and was not an obligatory moral responsibility. I didn't know that it was normal to feel confused and distrustful of myself and others after my innocence was taken from me.

I didn't know that to receive love, I didn't need popularity. I didn't know it was okay to boldly say no, and it wasn't my job to keep the peace. I didn't know that the term "boys will be boys" had nothing to do with me and there is no excuse for assaulting me, invading my privacy, and touching my body without enthusiastic consent from me. I didn't know that it's better not to be liked than to do things I'm not comfortable with just to feel worthy. Wearing short shorts, tank tops, or two-piece swimsuits did not make me dirty. I didn't know that it was my choice what to do with my body and that it was normal to explore curiosity early when you have older siblings. I didn't know that hormones and sexual feelings are a healthy part of puberty. That my body was perfect in every "awkward" stage of development and it was never a competition with other girls or women. That no amount of name brand clothing, makeup, or material things could possibly measure the beauty within. That my worth was not in the external validation I was seeking from the beginning.

I didn't know that the messages I received from church, culture, media, family, and friends about myself, my body, and my worth were deeply ingrained with distortions. I didn't know it was never my job to control the actions or thoughts of others. That when I did say no, a lot, it was his job to stop. I didn't know that virginity is a completely fabricated social construct to control women's sexuality to placate insecure men who abuse power and lack integrity. That religion was derived from the same fear and control tactics that have been around for centuries. That while there was truth in some of what I was learning, I had the right to choose what to believe. That as a woman it was not my job or duty to be submissive, meek, mild, quiet, and pure for the service of men and their pleasure. That I had a right to my pleasure. That the things I was being taught were largely the exact opposite of truth.

I didn't know because nobody told me. Looking back, I can see that intuitively on some level I did know these things. I wasn't taught to listen to my body or my intuition, so my inner knowing didn't align with what was in my mind. If any one of these things hit home for you, all I ask is that you pay it forward and share the truth. When we know better, we do better. So, let's do better together.

BEFRIENDING MY BODY

What I was taught about my body was all wrong. I haven't had a good relationship with my body for most of my life. I didn't know how to fully appreciate it when I was constantly trying to control or change it to fit a social expectation. It only started to change a few years ago when I began to realize I liked myself in old pictures better than current ones but remembered I was unhappy with my body at that time too. I also started recognizing how critical I was of my body when it allowed me to experience so much. It supported me in my outdoor adventures and allowed me to feel joy, pleasure, and beauty on so many levels. It serves me every day. And yet, I've learned to be unkind and critical of it. That just didn't make sense. I had believed the messages society gave me about what I was supposed to look like to be desirable and worthy of love.

Culturally, I was not taught to know my body, much less love it. Society taught me to be at war with myself and constantly try to change my body. As a teen, there was shame around the changes in my body, despite my health class that told me puberty happens to everyone and outlined what I could expect to see. It didn't prepare me for the social standards of beauty that were contradictory and impossible to please. It only worsened when I began to bleed. How embarrassing it was that every month for at least a week, I had to manage this painful, tiring, stressful thing that isn't ever talked about positively, and in most social settings, it's expected to be dealt with in secrecy! Going to the bathroom with a tampon tucked up your sleeve or asking to be excused in a whisper because you unexpectedly began to bleed. Girls aren't prepared enough to have a healthy relationship with their body, their womb, their yoni, and their moon. Boys aren't equipped with the information either, like how to respect what their female counterparts are experiencing and how to support them effectively. Of course, kids will get embarrassed and giggle at the uncomfortable things. But those boys grow into men, and at what point can we expect them to handle it maturely? I pray I get the opportunity to create a new way of doing things for myself and pass it down to the next generation of humanity.

As a collective, much of humanity has gotten disconnected from natural remedies for health and nutrition that are part of nature's design when we are in harmony with our environment. The cycle of life is built on abundance, but the way we have evolved has become toxic to ourselves and to our natural resources. I feel this imbalance in the air I breathe, the majority of food that is available to me, the health care I have received, and the cultural standards that are not in alignment with the wisdom of the body. I'm making amends with my body. I'm healing wounds from generational trauma and social conditioning that have been passed down through my lineage of women bearing the burden of patriarchal patterns of abuse, manipulation, and control. I'm coming home to the truth in my body that still lives there beneath layers of distorted thinking, indoctrination, and painful experiences. I am learning to feed it the nutrients it needs, internally and externally. This includes embracing my sensitivity to nurture my gut and digestion, my nervous system, and the quality of my breath and hydration. I seek out healing elements in my environment including nature, sounds, people, places, or experiences that are loving and nourishing. I am one with nature, and nature is me. The only way forward is getting back in harmony. It starts with me. Healing through the body with corrective experiencing releases trauma and sets the truth free.

Humanity is the way to expanded spirituality. We can remember we are spiritual beings of consciousness having a human experience and deeply embody that truth. The body is the pathway of humanity. Pleasure is part of that wisdom and sensuality is a tool for unlocking the magic we are capable of creating and experiencing. Our electromagnetic field is housed in the structure of the body. It's the most exquisite tool that allows us to experience beauty, joy, pleasure, pain, feeling. There is a lesson to be gained in all of it. Befriending my body has allowed me to restore balance to my own life as I learned to discern the ways it was communicating with me. I learned to recognize the signals my body was giving me when my nervous system needed nurturing. My intuition and experience have led me to tools that help me regulate my emotions, reduce stress, and honor the natural ebb and flow of my daily experience. As a sensitive person, I have been able to use my sensitivity as a superpower to guide me. This practice has allowed me to redefine my experience in a number of ways, shifting from sources of pain to strengths.

Here are some ways I was able to redefine my experience:

- Honoring my moon cycle vs. dreading, resenting, and suffering
- Accepting my body vs. comparing, controlling, or changing
- Loving my vulva and yoni vs. avoiding, blaming, or criticizing
- Exploring my sexuality and sensuality vs. suppressing or shaming

- Expressing my creativity and authenticity vs. hiding

- Embracing my sensitivity and emotionality vs. repressing, judging, or numbing

- Trusting my intuition and inner knowing vs. doubting

- Reclaiming my spiritual connection vs. outsourcing

- Developing my authenticity vs. conforming

- Exercising my power in boundary setting vs. people pleasing

I remember the day I held my stomach and chest with my hands and cried as I apologized. I remember the moment of realization after ending a relationship with a man who often compared me to other women and made comments that my appearance didn't match his preference. I remember recognizing what a toll it had taken on the little confidence I had been able to build within myself to feel comfortable in my own skin. I tried to adjust to his preferences in what I wore, how I spoke, and the things I did. I allowed that relationship to make me feel insecure instead of leaving him. I didn't understand how I could have allowed that to continue for so long instead of immediately ending it. I made a promise to myself to never be in a relationship that made me feel bad about my body ever again. I vowed to treat myself with love and respect and only choose partners who were interested in who I authentically am.

I became the lover I longed for in every way. I committed to being more loving toward myself with my self-talk, my touch, and my actions. I invested in my nutrition and started listening to the symptoms my body was giving me. I learned how to interpret them and began responding to what it needed. I started pausing any time I noticed myself being critical of my body. I placed my hands on my stomach and chest and repeated "I love you, thank you" to whatever I had been criticizing. I started using a mirror, looking myself in the eye, and saying, "I love you, I'm sorry for the ways I've been unkind." I wrote reminders on the mirror in my bathroom that I would see every day. I left more reminders by my front door that I'd see every time I would leave. I stopped competing with my body. In so many ways, I stopped forcing it to do things that didn't feel loving, from forgoing uncomfortable fabrics to eliminating excessive exercising.

I used to get frustrated with the limitations of my body–it was never good enough. I wasn't consistent enough in the gym or I wasn't fit enough, curvy enough, or strong enough. I'd get angry with my body for fluctuating. I have a female body, so its very nature is to fluctuate every month. I learned to see the beauty in the cycles and embrace the changes with loving responses. I created rituals for myself around the full moon and new moon and learned to recognize the way my body patterned itself after the moon and the tides.

What does this have to do with sexuality? Everything. It's all a spectrum and building blocks of loving myself more deeply helped me open myself to receive more pleasure, love, and joy than I could have ever previously imagined. I had to decide I was no longer willing to subscribe to the messages that made me feel terrible inside. I'm not interested in a narrative that tells me I need to change myself to be beautiful. Beauty is. I can magnify it, amplify it, express it. But the truth, at its core, is that it already exists. When I started believing that and living my life with that as my reality, my experience started to shift drastically.

It's been a long journey of ups and downs with my body. Literally. Again, cycles are a natural part of the female experience. It's ironic that it gets so warped by societal standards that women learn to judge themselves and believe that something is wrong with them for not being more consistent. As if it wasn't part of the beautiful design to be dynamic. My journey with my body has been one of learning acceptance and practicing daily to embrace my body as it is and love it. Deeply, unconditionally. After all, it is my lifelong companion. The relationship I have with myself is arguably the most important one I'll ever have. If we're hitched for life, we might as well learn to get along, right? More than just getting along, more than acceptance, I've reached a point of true amazement. I can honestly say I am in love with the incredible gift it is to be consciously inhabiting a human body. As a person who identifies as a woman and was born in a female body, I have learned to appreciate the unique gifts and privileges that come with that experience.

How did I get here? Lots of practice. The first step was awareness. I became more and more aware of the ways I was making my body the enemy, constantly criticizing it, or trying to change it. Every time I would look in the mirror, there was something I was judging or noticing as inadequate. A blemish here, an imperfection there, a patch of cellulite or unwanted hair. I was always noticing through my perfectionistic lens. Always sucking my tummy in and flexing my abs to seem fit or look thin. I might as well have been surrounded by mirrors because my mind was constantly occupied with comparisons.

It's funny though, because looking outward, I wasn't using the same lens. I noticed beauty and standards of perfection and compared my own shortcomings to them. Other women would all get credit for their unique strengths while I was painfully aware of my own flaws, which I tried to hide at great lengths. I became aware that I was holding myself to a harsher standard than anyone else. The things I would think about myself were things I would never say to a friend. Why was I any different? That was a big wake up call, alerting me to the distortions in my mind and the messages I had been fed from so many sources. But the worst part was that I had somehow believed them. I had internalized them as true and held myself to those standards, despite the numerous holes in logic and contradictions.

I also became aware of what had made me so susceptible to believing them. I had wounds from my early childhood that left me feeling inadequate and seeking validation. I wasn't equipped with the tools to realize that true validation comes from within. I spent years seeking approval, belonging, and fitting in. I wanted acceptance from my peers. And from boys? I wanted their attention. Maybe then I would feel good enough, wanted, and confident. When I realized these wounds, I was devastated by how much they had been ruling my life. On the other hand, I was incredibly relieved because I could also see I had the power to heal them. I didn't need anything from anyone to love them. It would take work and dedication, but now that all my energy wasn't being siphoned into seeking external validation, I had plenty to spare for my own prioritization.

I knew how to work hard and be intentional about what I had control over. I had gone to incredible lengths to be what others needed from me in all my years of people-pleasing. How much more rewarding it was when I was able to invest that same energy into pleasing me! Not to mention I was no longer up against the contradictions and expectations outside of me. The problem with people-pleasing is it's destined for failure–you can't please everyone. So, it's a negative feedback loop that reinforces the belief that you are not good enough. And so on, and so on.

How do I do it? How do I give validation to myself and invest that energy into me? Sensuality has been one of the most powerful tools I have used to heal my mind, body, and spirit. It is a mindfulness practice to connect with my body through my sensuality. I use the power of my mind to focus my attention away from my thoughts and into my body. It is a deeply personal and powerful experience to embody my consciousness with so much presence. I notice thoughts that come up around my body, my identity, my pleasure, my to-do list, and a million other things. I practice being present in my body with my breath, and I simply breathe. Then I begin interacting more intentionally by changing my breath patterns, breathing more deeply, and inviting more oxygen into my body. I feel pleasure and relief through my exhales as any tension I've been carrying begins to release. Where there was resistance, fear, or painful feelings, I begin to feel them replaced with peace. This peace brings gratitude for something as simple as my breath and present awareness.

My hands move intuitively to my chest with one over my heart and one on my belly. The warmth of my hands feels like a hug, as I'm holding myself in my hands with love. "Thank you," I say to my body and the Divine. "Thank you for this gift of being alive." I allow my hands to continue guiding as an extension of my heart. They caress my chest as my fingers graze my collarbones, neck, shoulders, and the space between my breasts. This touch is light, gentle, and kind. I am so grateful for this beautiful sensation of loving touch from my heart. I feel seen, I feel held, and I feel connected to the Divine.

The hand on my belly brings a distracting thought. "Suck in, I can feel the rolls there–that's not attractive." I pause and witness the thought. I choose to invite the feelings that come with the thought and tears fill my eyes. I feel the pain of the shame that has been so deeply ingrained. The pain that is held there in my belly, beneath the skin, is a distorted belief that, to be worthy of love, I need to be thin. Thinner than I am, regardless of my size, weight, or image–the standard of perfection leaves no room for exceptions. I witness the pain, I allow the heat to rise through my chest, through my tears, and accept the emotion as it's expressed. I tell my belly it is loved just as it is. It is worthy of love and expansion with each and every breath. It is worthy of rest and it no longer needs to contort itself, always sucking in. It is worthy of food and nourishment. My hand delivers this message with even more fervent presence. My fingers sink into softness, pressing gently into the embrace as my belly fills the palm of my hand. I allow it to expand even more fully as I breathe deeply. It feels good to embrace this new permission to be, to breathe, to take up space. To realize my worth is not earned, it simply exists.

This release brings an eagerness to celebrate more of my body, and my hands keep moving. Down to my womb, my lower abdomen where so much softness is held. Where my body has experienced the most fluctuation since I was in my early pubescence–a process I once resented, dreaded, and deeply misunderstood as a result of being misinformed. The heightened sensitivity, the aching, the buildup and release. The cyclical pattern of life and death that has repeated each and every month since my very first bleed. I visualize my uterus and the divine purpose it serves, not only in birthing babies but also dreams. This is the birthplace of my creativity, my unique expression, and my inner child-like joy. The place of my greatest healing, abundance, sweetness of life, pleasure, and intuition. So much power, beauty, and wisdom is held in this organ. This is my portal to the Divine through my sacred gifts of creation and expression.

There is also pain here. So much pain. There is also so much strength and resilience that my womb has carried to endure the harshness of a world that does not celebrate her gifts or respect her power, but instead represses her power and seeks to control and possess it. For so many years, this part of me was neglected, shut down, disconnected, and ashamed. My excitement for life was related to my ability to dream, feel pleasure, and receive. For so many years, I needed this softness, this power, and this beautiful gift of intuition and creation. And yet, it was locked away, out of reach, beneath layers of oppression. My hand cradles my womb, feeling the tightness from the fear of being seen, fear of expressing and embracing sensuality, not feeling safe to be held in all of her emotionality. Mood swings being feared, judged, and resented instead of being honored as sources of wisdom with courage for feeling. Fear of being wrong with doubt created from years of gaslighting. I witness her shame from being shut down, shut out, kept small, manipulated, abused, labeled, misunderstood, and misused.

The health benefits of befriending my body are worth mentioning. The more attuned I am to my body and the sensations I am experiencing, the more I become sensitive to the cues when something is wrong–or when something is right. This helps me recognize its signals and respond to its needs. If I am constantly cutting off from my body, trying to change it, or blaming it for its natural way of being, I am more likely to dismiss it when it's communicating with me. It also prevents me from taking care of it and responding to what it needs. These can be simple things like eating when I'm hungry, being mindful of eating when I'm not actually hungry, breathing fully into my belly throughout the day, and releasing any stress and tension my body is carrying. When I ignore or numb my sensations, I could be bypassing really important systems that function to keep me healthy and well. One of these benefits is cultivating an internal awareness called interoception, or the perception of sensations from inside the body. This awareness can be useful in recognizing warning signs of illness, emotional distress, danger, or dysfunction in the body. It can also be useful in recognizing signs of pleasure, intuition, safety, health, and joy.

When I pair this perception with awareness of emotions, I am able to discern signals for what I am feeling, like what I am needing or desiring, a lot more easily. My body is wired with an internal system of communication. The wisdom has always been there, but I've had to learn how to tune in and listen.

My body also has built in mechanisms for healing. My nervous system has two sides of the coin, one system for stress response that helps me take action in a heightened state and another for resting and recharging to repair after the stress is complete. Through my body's intuition and what I have learned intellectually, I have found practices to support my body's natural processes. I've learned to reduce stress and nurture my body through movement, nourishment, affectionate touch, laughter, creative expression, social connection, and emotional release. These practices show up in a variety of ways, but it was so validating when I read the research about how to nurture the nervous system and the strategies suggested affirmed what my body had already been telling me. When I hum or sing to myself in the shower and feel relief, it is actually releasing stress and regulating my body. When I dance and shake and feel the tension release, it is my body shifting to a different state of being. When I feel drastic improvements in my mood and physical health after orgasm or sex, it is a result of connection and hormonal releases that are a part of the body's design. When I walk in nature and take in all of the sensations, I recognize that it is a remedy to reduce and prevent depression. Listening to my body and tuning in to its wisdom has taught me more than a textbook ever could.

One of the most significant ways I have learned to tune in to my body has been through paying attention to the sensations I am experiencing and no longer dismissing them as neutral or random. A good example of this was with my menstrual cycle and the symptoms I used to assume were "normal" and something everyone experienced. I was raised with a narrative that periods are to be dreaded because they come with all kinds of uncomfortable symptoms and side effects. In the dominant culture where I grew up, hormonal birth control is the first remedy suggested for any woman experiencing difficult menstrual symptoms. I tried this method when I was younger and it was significantly worse for me, even after trying multiple types.

In my late 20s, I made my first appointment with a naturopathic practitioner who specializes in women's health. That was the first medical provider I have truly felt seen by. The intake form was comprehensive, not only for medical history but also for social, emotional, and contextual factors. I was asked about sensory processing details, emotional patterns, thought patterns, behavioral habits, nutrition factors, and trauma history. In the initial appointment, she asked about my answers and listened to my experience with additional questions to ensure she understood my situation. With every subsequent appointment, I was asked about how each specific symptom had changed or stayed the same, and treatment was adjusted accordingly. I've never had an appointment be less than half an hour. My symptoms significantly improved and I have genuinely felt my provider sees and cares about me and has taken into consideration contextual factors that have been affecting my body. My treatment has included a combination of western medicine and holistic health protocols. And perhaps the most profound, my menstrual cycle has become more predictable, balanced, and even enjoyable! I look forward to the time of rest, release, clarity, and intention-setting. I embrace the sensitivity of my body and the embedded wisdom it carries on a cellular level. There are so many things it does for me, I can't even fully comprehend the complexities of its daily functioning.

Throughout my cycle, there are times when my feelings or energy are heightened, especially during ovulation and menstruation, just as the tides change with the phases of the moon. There is wisdom to this analogy as I also experience energetic shifts around the new moon and full moon. It is a common practice to have rituals that correlate with phases of the moon, like setting new goals and intentions with the new moon and resting and releasing with the full moon. As I get in tune with my body and my own cycle, I become more aware of what is happening internally. I can create rituals around its fluctuations to honor my body and its ability to create life and birth my dreams into reality.

Leading up to ovulation can be used to set intentions and goals for the month. It's a great time to get clarity about priorities, desires, and visions for what I am calling in. Ovulation is a wonderful opportunity to use the extra sexual energy to devote to my dreams, goals, or intentions. Whether I am in partnership or single, I particularly like to pair this with a liberal solo sex practice and numerous orgasms. This energy can be dedicated to anything I choose to devote it to. Leading up to menstruation is a good time for taking aligned actions that support my intentions to move toward resolution or completion by acting as if it is already so and holding myself accountable to whatever I need to do. During this time, I might start to experience heightened emotional sensitivity which can be a gift in highlighting areas I need to pay attention to, identifying underlying needs, or staying in my integrity. Of course, it can also be possible to project my sensitivity onto others with heightened irritability, easily hurt feelings, and reactivity, but this is only one side of the coin for me to be aware of.

Menstruation has become one of my favorite phases to reflect on. For me, it has become a time for resting, recharging, reflecting, resetting, releasing, and going inward. It is a time of less doing, more being, and receiving nurturing and inspiration. I can prepare my physical vessel, give back to the earth, or collaborate with the Divine. Menstruation is not just a time for lost opportunities as the body sheds an egg and cervical lining that will not be used for a pregnancy or creating human life. Just as this tissue is not needed by the body, what am I ready to release that is no longer serving me? You could also view this tissue as sacred, with coding and physical properties that promote life, and it can be dedicated to any purpose I choose. If my intentions were not to birth a child, what have I been devoting my energy to? Can I release it with gratitude for the purpose it served as though I am giving birth to my creation? In some traditions, menstrual blood can be used as a fertilizer for plants or soil since it contains many of the same minerals found in plant food. A more abstract application of this might be setting an intention of preparation for the next cycle. As I release anything that no longer serves me, how can I harvest the crops that I have been growing or weed my garden for the next season? As I slow down and meditate, emptying my busy mind and observing my internal experience, can I "fertilize" or prepare the metaphorical soil where I can plant my seeds of intention for my next ovulation?

As I speak from my own personal experience as a female bodied woman, my intention is to highlight examples of honoring seasons and cycles in alignment with the body, discuss what is possible with intention-setting, and provide an alternative narrative for menstrual cycles with a more affirming lens. I would like to acknowledge that the language used here speaks to the physical experience of some female bodied individuals, that not all female bodied people have periods or ovulate, and not all people who experience periods identify as women. This section is not intended to define the experience of all women, all female bodied individuals, or any one type of person. It is only for you to define what kinds of cycles or seasons shape your experience and the intentions you'd like to set with them. My menstrual cycle is one of the ways I embody and connect to the Divine Feminine and my womb as a portal to the spiritual realm through seasons of creation.

Spiritually and energetically, a womb can be a term to describe the physical embodiment of the sacral chakra, which is the energy center associated with creativity and sexuality. I don't use the term womb as only a literal reference to a uterus, but in alignment with a secondary definition referring to "a place where something is generated." I appreciate the extension of this principle to apply more broadly, and the possibilities for people to make new meaning of menstrual cycles in relationship to themselves or their partner, and for anyone of any sex to consider how they might be able to honor the cycles of the moon (literally and metaphorically).

To my vulva and yoni–I'm sorry for neglecting you for so long. For not listening to what you were telling me. For not protecting you, nurturing you, respecting you, cherishing you, and honoring what you needed. For judging your appearance against meaningless, superficial standards. For shaming, criticizing, and resenting you. For ever believing anything other than it being a gift and privilege to embody you. Today, I vow to honor and celebrate you for all that you are and to live in love and truth.

To my period, my moon–you're not a curse but a gift. A shamanic opportunity and time for reflection, release, feeling my feelings, and connecting to my spiritual gifts. Creating visions, connecting with the Earth. I am the universe embodied, nature by nature, the elements flowing through me with cycles and seasons, each with their own beauty and purpose. I honor your wisdom and sensitivity, bringing excitement and energy in times of creation, and inviting me to slow down to rest and reflect with the rise and fall of the body's natural rhythms.

JOURNAL PRACTICE:

1. Write a letter to your body. Start with gratitude. What does your body do for you that you often take for granted? If you deeply loved your body for more than superficial reasons, how would you speak to it? How would you treat it? Write a love letter to your body as you would if that were already true. You might be surprised by what comes to you.

2. What is your ideal relationship? How does your partner treat you, see you, touch you, etc.? How can you start being a better lover to yourself? This isn't just about sex. It's self-talk, being true to your word and keeping your commitments, aligning actions with intentions, making yourself a priority, cultivating compassion, forgiveness, and accountability, engaging in acts of service or kindness, spending time doing things that bring you joy, taking yourself on a date, and deciding which beliefs do not align with love and letting go of them.

   Set your boundaries–spiritual, physical, emotional, and mental boundaries. Learn your no and practice it everywhere. Get really good at saying no. This is the only way to get to a full OMG, YESSS. Love yourself enough to say no. When it's hard. When it's scary. When it's disappointing to others. When it defies expectations or norms. The greatest responsibility you have is to yourself. This is not selfish. This is the only way you can really trust yourself and it allows other people to trust you too. When you honor your truth, you're less likely to act outside of integrity in shadowy ways (the parts of us we reject or deny due to fear or shame and as a result of the suppression–the ones that express in reactive or unconscious ways). This also empowers us to take responsibility for our experience. We cannot control the actions of others, but we do have power over what we say yes to, what we allow, what we accept as truth, and what we choose for ourselves. Women especially struggle with people-pleasing. I understand how hard it can be to use your voice and risk contention, judgment, rejection, or shame. You are worth it, your peace is worth it, your healing and growth are worth it, and your purpose and potential are worth it.

3. What is your relationship to saying no? Is it easy or hard for you? Where did you learn this? How has it impacted you in your life?

HANDS-ON EXPERIENCE:

Make the commitment to be kind to your body. Decide to no longer treat it harshly or critically. Give yourself grace for the fact that it will not change overnight and you will still experience critical thoughts and difficult emotions. This is a process of choosing how to respond every time you notice it happening. Notice the parts of your body that are the hardest for you to love. Every time you notice yourself having a critical thought, catch yourself and take a deep breath into your belly. Develop a practice of showing kindness and compassion toward your body. You get to decide what that looks like for yourself. Consider journaling your experience after doing this for a week and note any changes you feel.

PLEASURE
AS A DESTINATION

—— ·～◆～· ——

As a society, we have lost the innocence of our pleasure. Somehow pleasure has been distorted to be associated with being sinful, selfish, shallow, immature, gluttonous, or less spiritually evolved. The concept of hedonism is controversial but perhaps misunderstood. Pleasure when used to numb or disconnect from one's self is imbalanced. Distraction, escapism, or redirected focus are useful tools to create balance when used consciously and in conjunction with other states. Pleasure isn't balanced when it's used as an avoidance tactic to diverge from doing the work or experiencing pain. Pain can have great purpose and avoiding pain only leads to more suffering. Pleasure brings balance to our lives and bodies. Things get unbalanced when pleasure is sought mindlessly vs. mindfully.

Sexual pleasure has been especially restricted and shamed. There are strict conditions under which it is allowed to be enjoyed. Even then, the focus or purpose is often around procreation and pleasure is just a byproduct. It's something to be enjoyed by a man and sometimes a woman (if she's lucky) only after they are married. In patriarchal cultures, women have often been treated as possessions of men. The purity of women must be preserved, only to be claimed by a man after marriage. Men's sexuality is also seen as a woman's responsibility. Even before marriage, it's her job to manage his thoughts and keep them pure. If he has lust in his heart, she is to blame for evoking it. After marriage, it is her duty to please him and keep him from straying. The narrative is, if he doesn't get sex at home, he will get it somewhere else, and again, she would get the blame. These are the cultural narratives that are ingrained in women across the world. It's time for a change, for truth to be restored, and for our power to be reclaimed.

Pleasure is not always associated with eros (sexual energy), and even when it is, it is not inherently wrong, sinful, or dirty energy. In fact, this is part of the divine nature of our beings. Our bodies have such incredible capacity to experience joy and pleasure. If not for enjoyment, what is the purpose of life? Surely it can't be only to endure suffering and create more life, just so those lives can be spent doing the same thing. Right? I mean, if not for the beauty of love and celebration of what it means to be alive, what would be the point of life? Pleasure is our birthright. The only function of the clitoris is pleasure; it's part of the human design. Notice how I didn't say men's pleasure is your birthright–or anyone else, for that matter. Your clitoris isn't for anyone but you. It is a gift for you that you get to choose how to use, who to share it with, and what you accept as truth. Your body is your sacred vessel to explore and discover what it can do. Open your heart to the truth and allow the Divine to show you the light of what is possible to experience in this life.

Buddhism suggests that "life is suffering." I believe this is true, but it's not the whole story. Again, there are two sides of the coin. Life is suffering, but it is also pleasure and joy. I believe it's important to accept and acknowledge both pain and pleasure to achieve a balanced life, but where we put our focus can determine how we define our experiences. Pleasure-seeking isn't inherently a bad thing. It only gets imbalanced when it's used as an escape from suffering. Suffering also gets imbalanced when we take life too seriously and don't allow ourselves to experience pleasure, play, connection, and joy. If we don't treat pleasure as a priority, it's all too easy for life to become overly focused on work and responsibilities.

Joy is a powerful antidote to the heavy states we must endure and learn from. Without joy, love, inspiration, hope, beauty, and peace, all that would be left is enduring the suffering. Pleasure is the destination and the journey. There are so many dimensions of pleasure to be explored and enjoyed before any kind of explicitly sexual stimuli get involved. Orgasm is a beautiful byproduct of sexuality that is indeed pleasurable, but it is not the goal. Orgasms are just one aspect of the pleasure spectrum. If pleasure is the goal, it opens up an entire world of possibilities with infinite sensations to play with. Pleasure is so much more than sex. It's in all of your senses. It's the sun on your skin, a hot shower, a beautiful song, a soft blanket, an embrace of a loved one, the scent of fresh baked cookies, the sound of water in a stream, the color of your favorite flower, the taste of your favorite dish. Sensuality is giving mindful awareness to the pleasure we can experience every day, but may unknowingly overlook. It's about slowing down, taking your time to enjoy the little things, and discovering your own definition of pleasure in your body.

Physical pleasure, or sensuality, is a powerful pathway to creating or expanding the joy and beauty in our lives. This concept was revolutionary for me. As a sensitive child, I remember intuitively seeking out certain sensations that were pleasurable or soothing. I also remember being avoidant of sensory stimuli and being shamed or bullied for my sensitivity. Looking back, it's easy to see why the part that stood out was being sensitive to uncomfortable things. The narrative was that I was too sensitive, too picky, too emotional, or too much of something. My default focus became fixated on the downsides of my sensitivity. I couldn't see all the ways it was such an incredible gift for me. In adulthood, I have much more control of my environment, my boundaries, and the choices I make to surround myself with people and experiences that are supportive of my growth, peace, pleasure, and sensitivity. As I have embraced my sensitivity as a gift, I have been able to experience the pleasure, joy, and beauty that is possible when I lean into it. When I let my sensitivity inform my desires, goals, and dreams, the life I have created is much more fulfilling. I still experience suffering. I still go through uncomfortable things, face obstacles, and make sacrifices, but the end result is better when I make pleasure a priority in my life. If I'm going to live my life in a body that is this sensitive, I am going to find ways to use that to my advantage.

Mindfulness has been an essential tool to help me create pleasure in my life. No matter what I'm doing or where I am, mindfulness helps me be present in the moment and notice my experience without judgment. Sometimes, inviting more pleasure into my life is simply about noticing the good things that are already there. Sometimes pleasure is about deepening appreciation for the pleasant parts of being alive. Mindfulness can also help me disconnect from the chaos that swirls in my mind. Often, my thoughts will be occupied with the past or future and create stress. While it can be helpful to learn from the past and plan for the future, analyzing can overfunction to the point that I am not fully experiencing the present. The present is important because it's what is real, certain, and right in front of me. If I am not connected to the present moment, I am less effective at applying the lessons from the past or taking actions that will affect the future in a conscious way. When I create a state of being instead of doing, accepting anything I'm feeling without judgment, and simply breathing, noticing, and observing, it makes a drastic difference in my day. It may not change the responsibilities I have to face or fix the problems I have to solve, but it changes *me*. In the grand scheme of my life, I am the most powerful agent of change. When I slow down to breathe, notice beauty, nurture my body, and enjoy my senses–even in small ways–I am a more effective, balanced, and happier version of myself. I know it's cliché, but I have truly experienced the wisdom in the phrase "Stop and smell the roses" by enjoying the beauty in each day.

I'll admit, this practice looks different every day. Some days are much harder than others, but the importance of pleasure is the same. Some days, my pleasure is intense, joyful excitement. Other days, it's gratitude, rest, breath, and stillness. No matter what is happening in my day, I look for the ways life is trying to love me. In my religious upbringing, I grew up with the phrase "tender mercies" to describe ways that God shows love in the midst of our suffering. I haven't always resonated with this phrase because mercy comes with a connotation that suggests unworthiness that is too close to shame. My current view of God is not one of vengeance or punishment for sins, but rather that we experience consequences for our actions–both positive and negative. Sometimes bad things happen to good people and suffering is the result of others' actions, chance, or the larger constructs and complex ripple effects of life.

This view of suffering is neutral and does not call into question our deservingness of love. We don't go through hard things because we deserve to suffer as punishment for our sinful nature. I do believe that life, or God, is trying to love me and alleviate my suffering. Even when things don't make sense and I'm hurting, I believe loving Divine energies are always available to me, surrounding me, ready to help alleviate my suffering. It has been up to me to see this and practice being open to receiving it. So, I embrace my pleasure, I am grateful for the beauty my life affords me to experience, and I look for the ways life is trying to love me. Mindfulness helps me notice the little things, the synchronicities, and the sweetness and tenderness of life. Perhaps a more appropriate term would be "tender miracles" that are born of compassion. My ability to experience pleasure is part of my design. It is a birthright. It also allows me to more fully appreciate and experience the tender miracles in my life.

SENSUALITY PRACTICE:

At the beginning of your day, set an intention to notice beauty in the world. Take note of anything you notice or experience as pleasurable or beautiful throughout the day. When you notice something, practice slowing down to be present with that sensation. This is a mindfulness practice to expand your awareness of things you already experience but may overlook or miss. Notice how you feel and where you feel it. Breathe into the feeling and allow it to expand in your mind. Consider each of your senses and observe how you are experiencing that moment with each of them (sight, smell, sound, taste, touch). Keep in mind that pleasure can be experienced with more than the five senses. Pleasure can be emotional, mental, or physical. Take a moment to appreciate the beauty in the sensation. Soften into it. Allow yourself to enjoy it. Breathe in gratitude for that sensation and exhale any tension you might be carrying. Throughout the day or at the end of the day, journal your experience and the things you noticed. *For an extra challenge, practice expressing the experiences by describing them in detail or telling them as though they were happening in real time rather than just listing or explaining them.*

Bonus practice: Create your own experience by intentionally choosing something you find pleasurable and expand it with mindfulness (e.g., eat a luxurious piece of chocolate in a slow, intentional manner, and notice each sensation you find pleasurable).

SENSUALITY AS A GATEWAY
TO CREATIVITY

Illuminate your senses. Wake them up with your touch and bring them to life. Evoke your Divine Feminine essence and find ways to soften her into surrender. Melt away the hardness that has built up around her heart, the stiffness in her muscles, and the tiredness in her soul from giving, giving, giving. Such a beautiful gift it is to give, yet it is unbalanced without ever receiving. What is it the feminine longs for? To be seen, heard, cherished, and supported in meeting her needs. You can't give her those things without taking the time and making her a priority. You won't see her without looking, hear her without listening, cherish her without serving, or meet her needs without asking. So, tell me, how is your feminine doing? Do you know where to find her? How to invite her? The most powerful way I have discovered is through the body. Your sensuality. It's the most effective tool to really know her, appreciate her, invite her, love her, and honor her. How else do you appreciate Mother Nature than with eyes to see, ears to hear, lips to taste, skin to touch, and a nose to smell her beauty? Your pleasure is a profound part of being human. Embrace your pleasure and magnify your feminine.

Our bodies already bridge the gap between the physical and spiritual realm. We perceive spiritual cues and communication through our physical senses. Our conscious observation and awareness of them simply helps to decipher them. Women bring life into this world through their wombs. Our wombs, where we carry our sacral energy, can be interdimensional portals to create with the Divine. How do we nurture this creative energy? I feel the most inspired when I soften into vulnerability and allow myself to feel my feelings in connection with my body. When I am still enough, quiet enough, and calm enough, I am able to discern the message clearly.

Spirituality is not all that different from creativity. Creation comes from expression–from the heart, body, and feeling. If we're burnt out, shut down, or guarded, we won't be connected to inspiration or tools of creation. When we nurture our bodies, we are so much more receptive to creation and communion with the Divine. Sex is a combination of service and surrender, giving and receiving. We can embody both in the practice of sacred sexuality.

When we embrace our pleasure, it leads to joy and inspiration for creative expression. Embodying and moving (quite literally) through our emotions with self-expression brings relief from suffering and value in sharing our unique experience and perspectives. This also creates opportunities for connection through being witnessed and allowing ourselves to be seen. When we express ourselves authentically with vulnerability, including the entire spectrum of human emotions that we experience, we give permission for others to do the same and we create a sense of community. We are social creatures. We crave connection and belonging but the lack of vulnerability in our culture perpetuates shame, which leads to isolation, loneliness, depression, and anxiety. When we reconnect with our bodies and practice radical acceptance of our emotions, allowing our bodies to express freely, it allows our emotions to pass through without getting stuck inside us.

Emotions are often the reason we get disconnected from the body in the first place–from a pattern of avoiding pain to prevent suffering. The ironic thing is this pattern actually perpetuates the suffering by prolonging the inevitable need to move through the feeling. If we avoid painful emotions, we get stuck in a cycle of numbing and apathy and limit our ability to experience joy and relief. Similarly, if we are cut off from our pleasure and sensuality, it limits our creativity, inspiration, and a powerful medicine for balancing out the pain. Either way, if we are closed off or shutting down our feelings, it stifles our creativity. It breaks my heart that we are not raised with this understanding because it prolongs unnecessary pain.

As children, we don't have control over our environment, which means we can't always create safe spaces that are accepting of emotional expression. In many circumstances, it wouldn't be welcomed or supported and therefore would not be adaptive for a child to behave in this way. So, culturally and socially, we are conditioned to fear and repress emotions, hiding them and conforming in pursuit of belonging and acceptance through a process of internal rejection. We are not taught the tools we need to master our emotions, so instead we become enslaved by them. I have been no exception to this process, as I fell into my patterns of people-pleasing and self-abandoning as an adaptive response to my environment. It's a social tragedy that is entirely preventable and, thankfully, reversible. As adults, we can choose to remain stuck in cycles of avoidance and numbing or learn to feel through difficult emotions and practice ways to release them.

Growing up, I didn't have the tools or resources to meet my own needs or process my emotions fully. They were too intense to face so I learned to cope by neglecting them. As I grew older, they were still overwhelming to experience any time they would come to the surface. I felt consumed by them until I learned how to engage with them. I had to learn to separate myself from the emotion itself and realize I was the observer, experiencer, and perceiver of them. They did not define me. When I was able to practice this through mindfulness exercises, I was also able to engage with them differently, and I began to understand the needs that were beneath the intensity. Almost every time, the need is for my vulnerable, insecure pain points to be acknowledged, seen, accepted, and expressed. Only when I was able to hold space for my own emotions (rather than becoming absorbed by them) was I able to effectively witness and express them. I was the one showing compassion and love toward them. I was the one responding to the fear, the desperation, and the longing to be held and seen. I was embodying both parts—the pain and the soothing.

The permission to express through the body was everything. It was like giving my inner child the message, "It's okay to feel, to cry, to yell, and to be heard. Your pain is valid and real." I did this through cathartic movement—shaking, dancing, hiking, running, fucking, punching, throwing, and stomping in an intentional place and setting. I did it through sound—screaming, wailing, speaking, yelling, crying, moaning, and chanting. I did it through creation—journaling, singing, poetry, painting, songwriting, and instrument playing. I allowed myself to feel, locating it in my body and moving through it with expression.

Authentic expression is creativity. It is artistic and beautiful and unique. One pathway to creating is channeling your pain into whatever medium or outlet you need. The obstacle is the way. Your emotions may be blocking you from feeling connected to joy and creativity. You may have heard the cliché term "Feel it to heal it." I don't think this concept is complete. There are plenty of people who get stuck in the feeling, absorbed in the pain with no way out of the suffering. It's no wonder they resort to numbing, avoiding, and dissociating. Expression is the bridge. First, I had to notice and accept the emotion, surrender to the feeling, and give myself permission to express it fully. Creativity does not have to be arduous. There is no right or wrong way to do it. It's harder to create when it is forced or you feel pressured or stressed. Expression is a stress release, a coping skill, a method of creativity, and a way of restoring energy. Over and over again, this is what sets me free.

As in all things, there are two sides of the coin. If creativity only involved feeling painful emotions and embodying them, there wouldn't be enough peace. Surely, there is more to life than only suffering and finding momentary relief. Another pathway to creativity is through sensuality and inviting joyful, pleasurable feelings. Just as we can invite or allow our uncomfortable emotions to be felt and expressed fully, we can also invite and expand our experience of sensual pleasure and appreciation of beauty. Through this practice, I was giving myself the message, "It's okay to feel, enjoy, cultivate, indulge, and invite sensual pleasure. Your pleasure is a birthright, it's natural and beautiful." When I do this, I open myself to a state of inspiration and embodied joy from which I can create naturally with ease and playfulness.

Expressing these emotions is fun and exciting. I find genuine pleasure in expressing--it amplifies the sensuality as I allow it to be fully expressed through my body. Just as with painful feelings, embodiment and expression are key. And do you know what's interesting? The methods for expression are the same. I do this through joyful movement–dancing, hiking, running, bouncing, caressing, lovemaking, nurturing, touching. I do it through sound– singing, laughing, whooping, squealing, chanting. I do it through creation–journaling, poetry, painting, songwriting, instrument playing, cooking. After all, are catharsis and pleasure all that different? Is there not pleasure in catharsis?

When I have practiced this radical acceptance of my emotions and allowed them to be expressed through me, I have experienced magic in my life. I have found so much healing through speaking my truth and being seen after years of repression and self-monitoring. It's exhilarating to allow myself to be free in how I move, how I sound, and how I am able to just be in my full truth. When my emotions are no longer controlling me, I can express them, release them, and even invite them like playmates. The immediate relief is incredible. I am learning how to allow my emotions to come and go, just passing through my body. Not only that, but I have noticed how creativity is like a shortcut to a different state of being.

When I engage in a creative activity with my body, like dancing or singing, no matter what I was feeling at the beginning, I can feel the joy start to seep in. To get here, I had to be open to it–I had to be willing to choose it and fully commit to the activity. When I did, it was amazing what I was able to unlock and experience. I never knew that I could choose a feeling. I can't control the feelings I experience spontaneously or in immediate response to a situation, but I can choose how I engage with them, think about them, respond to them, and express them. And I can choose to create a state of being with my thoughts and actions that invite the feeling. The distinction between these two things is significant. I practice noticing, accepting, and expressing the emotions I am experiencing to release them instead of rejecting, controlling, or forcing them away, while simultaneously inviting another emotion in to play.

One of the first times I experienced creating a state of being was through a somatic emotional release practice. I was at a training learning somatic release tools and was introduced to the practice of pillow fucking. I know, it sounds crazy and weird and embarrassing at first. But I was open and interested in discovering how this practice could be effective. So, I embraced it fully and gave myself permission to express anger through pillow fucking. The anger I had been carrying was around my sexuality being shamed and repressed in my upbringing. There was so much pain and suffering caused by the shame around my sexuality and I was fucking angry (pun intended). As I felt the anger come through my body, I channeled it through these pelvic thrusting movements which I had personally never paired with anger (at least not consciously). It was powerful. Literally, I felt power surging through me. I was reclaiming my power. Suddenly, I was no longer angry. I was enjoying it. I was aroused by it. The feeling of freedom and relief was exhilarating and I found myself connecting to my desire and sensual pleasure. It was all within me. My movements were no longer fucking but evolved to lovemaking. I was making love with myself, embodying my emotions, allowing the energy to move through me, and fearlessly, unapologetically reclaiming my sexual energy. I was literally giggling with ecstasy at the beauty and simplicity of it. I was free. All because I allowed myself to be angry. I surrendered my inhibitions, leaned into an uncomfortable growth edge, and gave myself permission to really feel and *express* my feelings through my body.

Since then, I've expanded my practice of making love with myself to embody all kinds of emotions and energies. It's been a powerful practice for transmuting pain into pleasure. It has become a process for reclaiming wounded or repressed aspects of my identity. Anything I have historically not allowed myself to be, I invite into my practice of solo lovemaking and allow myself to embody that emotion and energy. It is deeply empowering, healing, and satisfying. As I have done this, I have felt my confidence grow with my willingness to authentically express myself and be seen. I feel inspired to express myself through dance, poetry, singing, and speaking. I trust the emotions that flow through me, realizing their value and purpose. I see how much healing they bring me, showing me aspects of myself I need to see and make peace with. The trust in my body has deepened with a gratitude and respect for the innate wisdom it has always had, but was buried beneath inhibitions from ego and society. I've realized that expression is the primary language of the body and its voice has been silenced and stifled for most of my life—until now.

Permission to feel my feelings and release repressed emotions from the past was only the beginning. I am clearing the cobwebs that have been stuck in my body and clogging up the channels for present experiencing, spiritual intuiting, receiving, communing, and future manifesting. The more of my past that I am able to set free, the more I am able to be present with joy, pleasure, and creativity. I have been able to integrate the wisdom and lessons from my past experiences and even express them playfully through song writing, poetry, dance, and sharing from an empowered place. I am able to shed identities that no longer fit for me that were built around protecting my vulnerability and sensitivity. This has allowed my authentic identity to emerge as a powerful, creative, sensitive, independent, unapologetic, compassionate, sovereign, sexual, sensual, spiritual, driven, bold, strong, resilient, playful, grateful, joyful, loving woman.

I still experience suffering. I still feel the full spectrum of human emotions. I'm still learning, healing, practicing, and becoming who I want to be. But I finally know who that is. And holy hell does that feel amazing. What a contrast it is from the woman I was trying to be, who I had learned to be, who I thought I was supposed to be. I am free to create the life I want to live, to evolve into the woman I desire to be—a woman who inspires me. I'm driven by passion, desire, creativity, and joy for life to continue learning and evolving. I'm no longer operating from a default place of shame, fear, proving, or trying to be worthy. I know who the fuck I am and nobody can take that from me. The thing that got me here, I can confidently say, was experiencing the truth of who I am in my body. It is because of my sensuality, sexuality, and authentic spirituality that I am able to express who I am. The experiences I have had in my body are what speak truth to me, where I commune with God, how I interact with the world around me, and where I feel the most inspired, happy, and free.

I've discovered there are multiple dimensions of creativity and expression. Sometimes I need to express something I am already feeling. These are the moments I am connected to a feeling and can channel it into an outlet with something to say, offer, give, share, create. The inspiration is not always obvious when I am in a feeling state. Sometimes I need to take action to let it out, like opening the door for the flow to come through. This usually involves choosing a creative activity like journaling, dancing, singing, or painting and going through the motions for the emotions to move. Expression is a major part of creativity. Another dimension of creativity is receiving and inviting inspiration by doing things that evoke emotion and beauty. This usually involves activities like meditation, sound healing, yoga, time in nature, connection with loved ones, prayer, reading, listening to music, playing with children, observing all of the little things, and being open to receiving love from the universe through beauty and synchronicities. Personally, the key to receiving inspiration from life and the Divine is living with an open heart, doing things that spark joy, observing, and listening. Receiving from the Divine is an intentional state of being–being open, grateful, and present with each moment in a state of mindful curiosity and compassion.

I allow myself to dance between both sides of the coin, recognizing the value in each dimension and honoring what I feel prompted to do in the moment. It is in honoring all aspects of self-expression that

I am able to create a flow state. It also empowers me with the tools for manifesting, which is an extension of creativity. Manifesting is the ability to design the life I want to live and creating my own reality. Life doesn't have to be passively lived. It can be created and played with. We get to interact with it.

One principle I've discovered to be true is the law of reciprocity. Essentially, this principle boils down to the idea that what I put out affects what comes back to me. If I live with an open heart and give love to the world and those around me, I will attract experiences that reflect that back to me. If I overextend myself without boundaries, this will also be reflected back to me in my experiences. Life is a balance of giving and receiving. Creativity is the same. Sometimes I will express, release, or offer a creation or service, and other times I will be still and go within, allowing myself to be an empty vessel, resting and observing my internal experience. Sometimes I will create and share my gifts and other times I will witness and receive the gifts of others. This process happens within myself and outside myself. Give, receive. Express, listen. Witness, be witnessed. Yang, yin.

The ability to receive is one of the incredible gifts of the Divine Feminine that is essential for creativity. If I am closed off from receiving, I will likely attract imbalance, burnout, and patterns of over-extending. This has been a pattern I've gotten stuck in as I've tried to gain control of my life and adopted the approach of hard work and hyper-productivity. On the surface, it doesn't seem like a bad thing. After all, it's needed and valued to help me succeed in the things I want for my life. But when it isn't balanced with rest, play, and receiving help, support, and nurturing, hard work and discipline can only take me so far. There is wisdom in the balance of life and nature of the heart: to give and receive. We can observe this concept in nature with symbiotic relationships between species and ecosystems. As we are a part of nature, interconnected with all things and wired to be social creatures, the principle is the same. We aren't meant to do everything alone without receiving connection and support from others.

Being caring and nurturing is lovely. It feels good to give and be helpful to others. But if we don't allow ourselves to receive, it not only cuts us off from resources and support that we need, it also robs others of being able to share their gifts. We are limiting the intimacy that can be achieved through mutual vulnerability and reciprocally exchanging energy. Have you ever seen someone struggling and you wanted to help so badly but they wouldn't let you? Have you ever loved someone so much but they couldn't receive the love you wanted to give them? Now can you think of a time when someone was really struggling and they reached out and shared they needed help? Can you think of the feeling when you see someone in their vulnerability and they trust you and let you in? Brené Brown shares in all of her research that vulnerability is the key to authentic connection, and authentic connection is the key to healing shame. Giving service is easy. Receiving is vulnerable. Sharing what you are confident in is easy; allowing yourself to express and be witnessed in your vulnerability is much more challenging. But when we express our vulnerability and allow our authenticity to be seen, we are giving a gift to others. It is a brave invitation to authentic connection and permission for them to be vulnerable too. Vulnerability is essential for authentic relating, for the exchange of giving and receiving reciprocally.

What does this have to do with creativity? My ability to be vulnerable affects how willing I am to express myself authentically and to be seen. My ability to receive nurturing, pleasure, and support directly affects the depth of the connection I am able to have with myself, others, and the Divine. If I am not open to receiving, I am not allowing the Divine to guide me, support me, and respond to me. Prayer is not a one-way street. It can be a conversation, a relationship, and a communion with the Divine as I express and open myself to receive. I receive inspiration mostly from my experiences of the world around me, my body, and my sensuality. If I am disconnected from my senses, I will not be as attuned to the channel through which the Divine communicates with me. My sensitivity is how I am able to notice little things, observe patterns, and track synchronicities. But I have to be paying attention. I have to be connected to my body. Pleasure practices not only help me nurture my sensitivity and develop an ability to recognize signals within my body, but it also increases my capacity to receive love, beauty, inspiration, abundance, and joy. Pleasure brings balance to the stressful aspects of life, opens up our sensitivity to perceiving and embodying beauty, and invites creativity as we begin to find inspiration everywhere and in everything.

Our creativity lies at the root of our feelings. We must allow ourselves to feel, breathe, experience, and receive inspiration to express and create from our authenticity. If I am not in touch with my sensuality, I am not in touch with the full capacity of my feelings, my ability to receive, or my creativity. There is a reason mindfulness practices are designed to create a mind-body awareness and connection. Sensuality is a mindfulness practice with an intention of experiencing pleasure and embodying a state of being open to receive. When I am full and overflowing with pleasure, love, and gratitude, creativity comes naturally. I naturally want to give, serve, nurture, and create because I am in an abundant, inspired state. Creation is a natural byproduct and way of being when we are embodied in our pleasure, joy, and love for life. Expression comes from embodying our emotions, embracing our sensations, and giving ourselves permission to move through them. When expression becomes the norm and a natural way of life, it invites more pleasure and joy, relief from suffering, and inspiration to play.

Creativity is play. It is pleasure. It is pain. It is authenticity. Creativity is the light, the dark, and everything in between. Creativity is different from productivity. It is a celebration of life and humanity, an appreciation for the beauty in all things, and a devotion to being instead of doing. This may be an important distinction between the feminine and masculine. The feminine expresses with feeling where the masculine explains with logical understanding. Both are beautiful and necessary. It is a marriage between mind and body. I believe there is wisdom in the fact that we are consciousness embodied. As we connect to our sensuality, it allows us to access our intuition, our sixth sense, the spiritual gift of the feminine. Our conscious observation and self-awareness of our bodily sensations allow us to create with intention and appreciate the fruits of creativity more fully. Our embodied experience allows us to apply what we intellectually comprehend and gain wisdom in the process.

The only way you can integrate this wisdom fully is through experience. For me, this happens when I am embodying my pleasure and joy and living a life that inspires me. It happens when I witness the artistic expressions of others through authentic relating, reading, poetry, music, and natural beauty. Explore your own sensuality, nurture and play with your body, surrender to pleasure, cultivate your own sensitivity, practice your own vulnerability, allow yourself to feel and express your feelings, exercise creativity, embrace your curiosity, and open yourself to receive pleasure, inspiration, joy, and clarity. Engage with the world and allow yourself to receive pleasure. Remember it is not only through painful feelings but also pleasurable ones. Mindfulness can be an open invitation to both.

Accept whatever comes up and trust that either way, you can move through it in service of your highest good.

The more you explore and discover what works for you and your body, the more sensitive you will become to your sensuality. The more connected you are to your sensuality, the easier it will be to recognize the prompts for what your body wants and needs. The more you honor what your body wants and needs, the more you will feel pleasure and relief. The more you feel pleasure and relief, the easier it will be to trust yourself and let your body lead. The more you trust and accept your body and feelings, the easier it will be to embrace your vulnerability. The more you embrace your vulnerability, the easier it will be to express your authenticity and expand your creativity. The more you express your authenticity, the more joyful and playful your creativity and life will be.

This is a practice. I've had to give myself permission to open my heart to feeling each moment, eliminating distractions, and surrendering the urge to force it. There are still times I want to create a state of being and it feels more effortful than just connecting with my body and allowing it to lead. In these moments, I pause and ask myself, "What does it want to experience? What movements, sounds, and activities are inspiring?" I have learned to trust that my body will lead me to my highest good, giving me what I need instead of what I think I need to do.

Accessing creativity can take a while if it's not a regular practice. It's still a work in progress for me as I learn to come back to stillness when the world is busy and my life is filled with to-do lists and responsibilities. When I don't make it a priority, it takes me longer to clear myself of all the busy thoughts and automatic habits instead of being heart-led and aligned with my soul purpose. Nature is crucial for me to clear my mind and allow my body to disconnect from the chaos of technology and the city. Being in nature helps me come home to my true essence. How easy it is to forget. Without daily practice, I forget what it feels like to embody joy, connect to my body and nature, and feel inspired as I create my day instead of living it or enduring it from a habitual place. So, as a regular practice, I start my day with something that sparks joy. I get into my body and do something that invites sensual pleasure and emotional release. It can be anything. Some of the experiences I've had look a little bit like this:

Dancing on the beach, singing in the rain, and stomping my feet on a wood floor—sending a rippling sensation of vibration beneath me. Finding a flow state of pure expression and joy. Bare feet sinking into fresh green grass, full belly breaths with a rhythmic rise and fall of my chest, music flowing with drumming, humming, and harmonizing, verbal journaling, or creative writing. Sound healing, sensitive feeling. Using all of my senses to heighten my experiences. Living life as a ceremony, offering presence to the beauty in the details through setting intentions and thoughtfully crafted rituals. Creating food, connecting to community, laughing together, dancing and singing. Playing in nature, exploring and adventuring. Feeling connected to the elements and being open to receiving their energy. Feeling soft, inspired, and free. Making love to life. Sitting beneath a tree, listening to music or the sound of the breeze as it drifts through the leaves. Feeling the spongy nature of grass, the cool dewy drops on each blade. Soaking in the purple tips of succulent leaves, tiny daisies, clovers, or feathery weeds. So many varieties of life springing forth from the earth, each one unique in the beauty it brings. Slowing down and appreciating all of the little things, exploring the infinite ways I can interact with the world through my sensuality.

EMBODIED EXPRESSION EXERCISE AND JOURNAL PRACTICE:

Create a space where you'll have privacy and safety to express yourself completely, without fear of being judged. Reflect on the following questions:

1. What am I feeling?

2. Is it pleasurable or painful?

3. Where do I feel it in my body?

Practice allowing it to be there and observe it without judgment or pushing it away. Breathe deeply as you observe it. Allow yourself to notice and experience any emotional response that happens as you allow the feeling to be felt. How can you express this emotion? What does your body want to do with it? If you don't know, that's okay. Just ask your body and notice what comes up.

Allow yourself to sit with the uncertainty and create space for the answer to come or experiment with different expression tools in your body. You might let yourself cry sad or joyful tears, breathe deeply and exhale the feeling, make a sound or vibration in your body (sing, hum, chant, sigh, squeal, whoop, holler, scream or yell, moan, groan, wail, sob), move your body (rock, shake, bounce, swing or sway, walk, run, stretch, do yoga, dance), hit something (drum, clap, snap, punch a pillow, kick or hit the air or a punching bag, throw pillows at the ground or a wall), have an excited or angry tantrum (stomp your feet, clench/pound your fists), fuck your pillow or make love to your body, write it down or speak it out loud in a stream of consciousness style. The most important thing to do is listen to your body. A good rule of thumb is if it hurts, don't do it. Journal your experience. Describe the feelings, sensations, and thoughts you notice throughout the exercise. Even if this practice only helps you become more aware of inhibitions or blocks you might have that prevent you from expressing yourself more freely, that is success! Journal about what you notice and consider reflecting on where you may have learned that response. How has it served you in the past? Was there a time you needed it to protect yourself? Does it still serve you? Why or why not?

Disclaimer: I am not responsible for any potential injuries that occur during this exercise.

CREATE YOUR OWN PRACTICE:

Consider the following: *What do you feel inspired by? What makes you feel alive?* This is the root of creativity–following inspiration from your senses and doing something from a place of feeling. Here are some ideas to get your started:

Start with music that makes you feel alive. Set a mood. Create a vibe. Add movement–dance, stretch, bounce, shake. Play with sound–drum, hum, play an instrument, or sing. Get in your body and create a sensual state. Light some candles. Run a bath. Romance yourself. Enjoy your naked beautiful body wrapped in a fuzzy blanket, run velvety rose petals across your skin, caress your entire body with your beautiful hands with love, tenderness, and juiciness. Open yourself to a state of inspiration, then follow your flow with complete surrender to what you feel called to do. Write, sing, move, draw, paint, cook, bake, or do anything else you feel inspired to create. Express yourself through being in a flow state.

RESOURCES:

If it feels overwhelming to create by yourself, start with a guided experience! I'd highly recommend trying the Kinrgy method. You can access virtual classes at kinrgy.com. Another great virtual resource is Chakradance with Natalie Southgate, which includes a guided movement practice as well as a beautiful guided imagery meditation to balance each of the seven chakras. You can access it online at chakradance.com/chakradance-daily-practice/.

For more information about how trauma or emotional pain is stored in the body and how to release it, I'd recommend the following books:

- *Waking the Tiger* by Peter A. Levine

- *The Body Keeps the Score: Brain, Mind, and Body in the Healing of Trauma* by Bessel van der Kolk

ORGASMAGIC:
THE HEALING POWER OF SOLO SEX

When I wasn't connected to my own pleasure, arousal, desire, and body, it was really difficult to express my desires and needs. This prevented me from receiving the fullness of pleasure in intimacy. This disconnect was paired with the self-abandoning tendency of being preoccupied with my partners' needs. I was so focused on getting validation from both pleasing them and being desired by them that I wasn't tuning in to myself and my body to ask what it was desiring. I didn't give myself full permission to request what I wanted or have healthy boundaries.

For example, I would often rush through foreplay, going along with my partners' speed. I didn't give myself space to nurture my arousal or take pleasure in the journey. I was lucky, because I was familiar with my clitoris and my body was able to "catch up" pretty quickly and achieve orgasm during intercourse, but I was still disconnected from my own sexual energy and experience.

The game changer was taking ownership of my solo sex practice. When I was the only partner to please, I had space to consider what my body really craved. It was just me, my body, and my imagination. Foreplay became everything from mental imagery to deep nurturing, soft caressing, teasing and anticipation building, to all kinds of variety of sensations, inspirations, and energy.

The last one—energy—was particularly important to me. Before I discovered how energetics could play a role in my solo sex practice, it was a purely physical stimulation that would lead to a physical climax. But now I know that when sex only involves physical or genital stimulation, it's uninspiring to me.

It's obvious to me now, as a highly sensitive and emotional being, I need more than purely physical contact for sex to be fulfilling. I need connection, intimacy, sensual sensitivity, and energetic alignment. For a long time, I intuitively knew this about myself; I didn't have language to articulate it, but my body knew. My heart knew. I was deeply unfulfilled sexually when I was single because I thought I couldn't have these things without a consistent partner. I was also often unfulfilled in partnership because I wasn't communicating my desires and needs well, and I was relying on my partner to fulfill them. My heart aches for those past versions of myself when I didn't know how to get my needs met, and for the partners who were doing their best to create intimacy with me as they sensed my frustration and felt inadequate.

Since discovering these things on my own, I've learned of the Erotic Blueprints framework established by sexologist Jaiya. It suggests there are different styles of sexual arousal for different people based on a number of factors, broken down into five blueprints. For people who have a predominantly sexual Erotic Blueprint, physical stimulation of the genitals is perfectly satisfying. As I've explored my own blueprint layout, I've discovered my primary Erotic Blueprint is energetic! I have fairly high degrees of sensual, kinky, and shapeshifting too, but my least developed category is sexual (aka purely physical stimulation). This framework has helped me understand myself, my desires, and the types of stimulation that help me achieve arousal and, ultimately, orgasm. I didn't know about it for a very long time, so it was a lot of poking around in the dark, if you know what I mean.

Had I not explored my sexual pleasure on my own, I would have never discovered so thoroughly what I prefer and the best ways to please me, and would have continued focusing on my partners' pleasure and neglecting my own needs. Ironically, as I became familiar with my own sexual needs, the shared experiences with a partner also improved. I now know what I like and have learned to communicate it with my partner. As it turns out, being connected to my own pleasure is quite the turn-on for my partner, and the mutual pleasure we can create together is infinitely better.

There are many types of orgasms with varying levels of intensity, and many women are capable of having *multiple* orgasms with very little time between. Of course, I'd love nothing more than for every woman to know the bliss of full-bodied ecstasy after having as many orgasms as she pleases, but there's nothing pleasurable about feeling stressed or pressured to have multiple orgasms (or even one for that matter). When sexuality becomes goal-oriented with orgasm as the destination, it creates pressure and puts expectations around pleasure. This pressure can actually be a deterrent for experiencing an orgasm and enjoying the experience. I've found the best approach is to slow down and focus on pleasure as the goal, savoring all of the sensations from arousal to climax. When I take my time with arousal, my pleasure in the process and the quality of my orgasms are significantly better.

Ultimately, there is no right or wrong way to experience pleasure. As I have now experienced a wide range of pleasure and orgasms, I've learned to appreciate the variety and enjoy discovering my personal preferences of contexts, dynamics, stimuli, and fantasies along the way. My investment in getting to know my body and exploring my own sensuality has greatly expanded my capacity for the amount and variety of pleasure I'm able to experience.

My journey with my solo sex practice reminds me of my journey with hot baths.

For most of my adult life, I could not understand what people liked about sitting in hot water for a prolonged period of time for the purpose of relaxing. It's not even in an inspiring setting, like in a hot tub where you're outside and warm while enjoying the scenery. Whenever I tried relaxing in a bath, the only outcome I experienced was feeling hot, sometimes even sweaty, which seemed counterproductive to me. I'd sit there until my hands and feet were pruney, and give up after I felt I had been there long enough to justify all the water I'd used filling up the tub.

I didn't understand what the hype was until I figured out how to *create* an inspiring setting. I'd design the vibe, light some candles, pair some music with the mood, set an intention, and add magic to the water with bath salts or a scented bath bomb that would feel like silk against my skin. I started meditating, breathing, and releasing emotions and energy that weren't serving me. I started nurturing my body with the ritual I was creating. *That* was pleasurable. *That* made it click for me.

My solo sex practice had to be the same thing–an opportunity to create an inspirational setting that truly nourished every aspect of myself. In fact, a major reason I compare these processes is because I remember being in one of these luxurious baths–caressing my body, using my breath and imagery to clear my energy–when I felt inspired to expand into my solo sex practice intentionally. I started flexing my pelvic floor muscle with my inhales, drawing in energy through my yoni and up my spine to the crown of my head. I'd exhale and relax, releasing stagnant energy, and do it again.

It was a natural progression of arousal and the imagery came intuitively as I imagined what I wanted to penetrate me. What was I drawing in? What was I inviting into my yoni? The answer came: Divine Love and healing energy. Mental imagery is a powerful thing. My body knew the sensation of penetration and it was experiencing stimulation as I was breathing and flexing my pelvic floor muscle. The combination of these things made it real. One of my mentors taught me that *my hands are an extension of my heart.* Remembering this, I allowed my body to show me what it needed through expressing, exploring, and experiencing, and it truly felt like my heart was nurturing me through my hands. When I added clitoral stimulation, it was over. I was in utter ecstasy. I had experienced my first orgasm on my own that was completely satisfying. I wasn't left wanting. It was extremely liberating, and after that day, my solo sex practice has never been the same.

Once I discovered I could have delicious, inspiring, life-giving orgasms on my own, there has been nothing but play and expansion in my sexuality. I experienced orgasms before, but the ones I've discovered through my solo sex practice have been next level. Now, all I have to do is be open to receiving. Open to receiving pleasure, inspiration, beauty, love, and joy. Opening myself to these things is a choice, a receptivity, a prayer, and an invitation for the Divine to commune with me. I trust my body, desires, emotions, and anything that sets my heart on fire. I follow my pleasure into ecstasy and allow it to lead me to healing. As I do this, I am no longer chasing something, there is no longer lack or wanting, it is only inviting and being open to receiving.

My invitations require action. I must be willing to surrender into softness, to nurture my body and listen to its needs. I have to give myself permission to embody and express anything I feel inspired to do or be. This is particularly true regarding things that excite me but we often carry judgments around, including taboo kinks we "shouldn't" enjoy. I no longer judge any part of me that comes through as there is nothing shameful about things that arouse me or excite me. I trust my joy. I trust my pleasure. I trust my body.

Shame doesn't serve me. Its only value is to show me where I need healing. In the past, I felt shame *after* my orgasm because of a distorted belief that pleasure was wrong or bad. Noting the timing of the emotion is significant because it helped me discern that the shame was related to a judgmental belief about pleasure, as opposed to the experience of pleasure itself. As we learn to listen to our intuition, we get to choose what we accept as truth based on our own experience (e.g., "Does pleasure serve me?" or "Does the belief I have about pleasure serve me?"). In this case, my belief was the source of my distress and confusion because it was so different from my experience. My internal judgment told me orgasm and pleasure were all a part of the carnal sin I was committing. This belief was not serving me. Not even a little bit. When I allowed myself to challenge it, to compare it to what felt true to my experience, I was able to discern for myself what I personally believed about my orgasms. And let me tell you, I'm *so glad I did.*

By exploring my sexuality through solo sex and in loving partnerships, I created corrective experiences for myself. A shameful belief or learned response can be replaced with a new truth through a positive new experience. When my heart is open and filled with curiosity, I am allowed to discover what feels true to me. In this process, my orgasm has served as a confirmation and amplifying energy; it reinforces new truths and helps me release anything that doesn't serve me. Now I sometimes wonder if I'm a bit of a masochist as I actually get excited when I notice shame! But that's because I know that just on the other side of shame is freedom and healing.

My sexuality has become a road map that shows the direction I need to go. The more I let go of the judgment of my pleasure and the self-monitoring that tells me what is right or wrong in my own body, the more open I am to corrective experiencing. I am always learning. There is a lot I don't know, and part of being human is making mistakes. Instead of responding to mistakes with shame, I now have an expanded capacity to forgive and love myself, learning from my missteps instead of condemning myself for them. This creates space to integrate the lesson and align with awareness, accountability, and integrity.

"Shadows" are parts of ourselves we have cut off or rejected, and are therefore unconscious of. We all have shadows. Shame keeps our shadows in the dark where they operate in stealthy, wounded, unconscious ways. Freedom comes from integrating them, accepting all parts of ourselves, and responding with love and permission to express what they need and desire. At the core of each shadow is an opportunity for healing. Sexual fantasies can be a powerful tool to embrace our shadows and allow them to play out hidden desires without judgment.

I'd like to be clear that embracing fantasies doesn't always mean acting them out and making them reality. Embracing fantasies simply means mentally allowing yourself to trust your desires and arousal to lead you to pleasure and beauty. One thing I have heard often on my healing journey is "there is no thought police." This was profound for me because part of the purity culture I was raised in emphasized the importance of keeping my thoughts pure and clean to be spiritually "worthy." This was one of the pieces that reinforced the idea that sexual thoughts and feelings would create separation from the Divine. As I have embraced my fantasies and the sexual energy that comes with them, I have experienced more pleasure, orgasms, inspiration, and creativity, deeper love for myself, and a deeper connection to the Divine. I now see my fantasies as a tool for unlocking my sacral chakra and tapping into my sacred sexual energy.

There is healing power and wisdom in our fantasies. They provide us with opportunities for energetic role-playing. In my solo sex practice, fantasies have provided the most profound corrective experiences and shifts in the way I relate to my body, my sexuality, and the world around me. When I have embraced and integrated every aspect of my being, including shadow parts of myself that I previously rejected in shame, I have felt whole, empowered, and loved. Not only do I feel more love for myself, I feel more aligned with my authentic self: a multi-dimensional being with both light and dark elements.

A major aspect of fantasy play involves embracing my own kinks. A kink can be anything that might be perceived as socially taboo, which makes it rather subjective. In my own experience, it was not socially acceptable to be sexual, so embracing sexual desires made me "bad" and "dirty." I also found these forbidden territories rather exciting. I developed a kink around sexual rebellion and became aroused by "dirty talk" and the fantasy of breaking the rules or being naughty. When this aspect of myself was in shadow, it led to me acting outside of my integrity and getting into situations that didn't serve me. When it was a rejected part of me, I didn't carefully choose which rules were fine to break and which ones were ethically important to me. Instead, it played out more impulsively and led to consequences that were harmful to myself and people I cared about.

One variation of this was arousal from being dominated or corrupted. This was especially appealing because it involved breaking rules by surrendering control, creating the illusion of not having choice. It's quite ingenious when you think about it–my subconscious created a way for me to embrace my sexuality without having to overtly act on my desires, therefore preserving my innocence. In my mind, I might have even been able to justify it to God as I plead my case.

The problem was, when I couldn't embrace the fact that this was actually *my* desire, it became stealthy, and I felt attracted to partners who were also in shadow. I was attracted to men who were dominant, possessive, controlling, and comfortable with convincing me to say yes after I had already said no. They were also the type of men who didn't care what kinds of relationship agreements I had, and the layers of forbidden territory compounded. In shadow, this kink did not serve me. Instead, it reinforced the narrative that sexual desires are sinful, wrong, and dirty. I was ashamed of my actions, felt disempowered, lost respect for myself, and denied my sexuality even more.

When I was finally able to embrace this aspect of my sexuality, it was extremely liberating. I realized I could integrate these desires in an empowered way, starting with my own fantasies. While there is something incredibly hot and exciting about forbidden sex, the consequences of acting on those impulses are less hot and exciting. Often, the reality is less satisfying than the idea itself. That's what makes it a fantasy. As I allowed these desires to exist in the realm of my fantasies, I was able to enjoy the thrill without the consequences. Here I could observe them with curiosity and learn what I desired to actually *experience*, allowing me to express my desires consciously. Consciously, I enjoyed surrendering control, being dominated, and breaking rules, but in a safe way with mutual respect, consent, and integrity. I could choose which rules I wanted to break and which ones I wanted to maintain. My solo sex practice became an act of conscious rebellion. After all, I wasn't *supposed* to do that. Now I enjoy breaking that rule almost every single day– sometimes multiple times a day!

Embracing these hidden desires also allowed me to act on them with integrity in partnership and gain even more clarity. I learned that domination and submission can be a very fun, safe, and ethical way to play out fantasies with power dynamics when both partners are consenting and respectful of boundaries. Exploring with my partner has been a way to examine dynamics of giving and receiving in our relationship and taught me how diverse and nuanced my desires can be. I've learned that my desire for a partner to be assertive and take the lead isn't always about submission and giving up control, but can also be about initiation, surrender, and validation. My partner initiating and telling me exactly what he wants reassures me that I am desirable and I know how to please him. I have also found *I get pleasure* from pleasuring my partner in devotion. Isn't that interesting? Sexually pleasing my partner is about me. Through experience, I learned to distinguish between dynamics of giving and receiving. When I am in the receiving role, I get to direct my partner to elicit my arousal and help me surrender into my pleasure. As I got familiar with these nuances, I was able to experience multiple dimensions of myself that brought balance and healing.

This acceptance and liberation of my desires helped me reclaim my own power and integrity, release shame, and taught me more about myself and my authentic desires for pleasure. The corrective experiences I was able to have from a place of open curiosity taught me my sexuality wasn't bad or dirty after all, but quite beautiful. The shame was actually the cause of the shadow. When I can slow down and lean into the feeling, surrendering the judgment and allowing myself to embrace the excitement, my orgasm can liberate the desire from the depths of shame and bring it into the light.

Some people might fear the idea of embracing all sexual kinks, worrying that doing so would lead to an increase of violent or abusive behavior. But we can embrace fantasies and arousal with curiosity and acceptance, while continuing to manage our actions with ethical integrity. It is when desires and taboos are in shadow that they create the most harm, including those related to sexual abuse. Sexual desires and fantasies are different from actions or intentions to act. Rape fantasies, for example, are incredibly common, but they don't automatically mean a person desires to actually be raped or to sexually violate another person. Part of our wild nature is to have elements of both predator and prey. The human psyche is complex with light and dark elements. Accepting that we all have both is how we reach wholeness and liberation.

Sexuality is no different. Our *nature* is not inherently wrong, but how we *engage* with the nature of our being can make all the difference. We get to choose how we relate to it and how we behave. Enjoying the idea of something doesn't directly translate to me wanting to experience it for real. And even if I *desire* to experience something, it doesn't directly translate to having an intention to act on that desire. I might desire to have sex with someone other than my partner or to have a threesome with my partner and another lover at the same time. If my partner doesn't share that desire, I choose to respect his boundaries and maintain the trust and safety of the relationship, which is more valuable to me than acting on the fantasy. I can still enjoy those fantasies and desires in my solo sex practice and choose what I act on according to my integrity, with respect for the ethical consent, agency, and well-being of others.

Accepting sexual fantasies, no matter how dark, twisted, strange, or abnormal they may seem can reduce shame around sex and help prevent harmful behavior by creating opportunities for understanding and healing. Removing the blame from sexual fantasies, desires, or urges can create a context for understanding and treating the complexities of underlying mental health issues related to harmful sexual behavior instead of compounding the problem with more shame. Instead, we can focus on consciously healing and integrating all aspects of ourselves with compassion so we can explore freely without compromising integrity. After all, sex is one of the significant ways adults play and create! Doing shadow work can liberate us from shame and make sex fun again.

Another way my orgasm has been healing is through reclaiming power and bringing balance to insecurities.

Shame is often wrapped around distorted beliefs that reinforce insecurities. I've noticed my insecurities can get stuck in my body, manifesting with physical discomfort, tightening, or contracting. A good example of this is the practice I mentioned earlier when I noticed the pattern of sucking my belly in. This was the physical manifestation of shame stemming from a belief that I am not good enough as I am. The first step in overcoming this shame response was becoming aware of it and responding with acceptance and compassion. The more practice I got being present with this emotion and contraction, breathing consciously into my belly and allowing it to expand, the more I was able to soften and relax.

During a self-pleasure practice one day, the familiar contraction happened as my hands were caressing my skin and feeling the curves of my lower abdomen. In response, I slowed down and softened my muscles. As my body relaxed, I was able to expand into the pleasure of my own softness. I was actually able to *enjoy* the feel of my belly as my fingers pressed in and grasped a handful of my skin. I suddenly came to understand the eroticism of soft curviness. I was enjoying the sensation of my open palm pressing into my belly, the other hand finding its way to my thighs, ass, and breasts. Each sensation was a confirmation of arousal from my own softness. I wasn't conforming, contorting, or performing. Instead, I felt sexy by embracing my authentic body in that moment, and it was amazing. As I continued to build my arousal, I made love to my body in its true form and my orgasm gave birth to a new belief: "I am so fucking sexy just as I am."

I'd like to point out the key concept here is self-acceptance in all forms, all phases of life, and all shapes, sizes, and dimensions. When I talk about embracing my curves, I don't mean the tight muscular curves that are built in a gym. I do feel sexy when I am fit and strong and muscular from working out. I feel beautiful when I have well-defined thighs, abs, and arms, with perky breasts and a hard-earned booty. There is nothing wrong with those things, but they only represent a single dimension of beauty. Those versions of my body are easier for me to accept and find sexy because they align more closely with the socially accepted standard of beauty, but I have had a much more difficult time loving myself in my softness. So it was empowering to not only feel an acceptance of my body in this practice, but to experience pleasure and feel sexy in my being. Cultivating gratitude for my body and everything it does for me, including pleasure, was the foundation of my healing. My gratitude allowed me to feel authentic love for my body and helped me expand my pleasure as I caressed my curves and deepened into my sensuality.

I no longer tolerate shame about my body. Instead, I accept the pain caused by shame and allow it to transform into something new. My orgasms help me alchemize my pain into pleasure, insecurity into confidence, and distortions into truth.

This principle applies not only to beliefs about my body, but also to aspects of my sense of self. When I practice being in tune with my sensuality, it also cultivates an awareness of pain points that my body carries emotionally. I can use my orgasmic energy to rewire my beliefs to align with my highest self. I am worthy. I am loved. I am powerful. I am supported. I am creative. I am strong. I am enough. I am valued and cherished. These affirmations are especially powerful to connect to during my solo sex practice when I invite the Divine as a lover. The divine truths of my being are brought to light and amplified through my pleasure and orgasm.

Your orgasm is your magic. It's your power—your portal to the Divine. Your pleasure is directly linked with your creative flow in life. You have a human birthright to your pleasure and feminine pleasure is directly linked with your creative flow. A feminine essence offers gifts of softness, sweetness, and goddess embodied truth. But feminine embodiment is not just soft and sweet. It can also be fierce, strong, and powerful. It is a force to be reckoned with, like the raging sea that demands presence and moves unapologetically in her truth. The feminine expression does not have one expression, but infinite. You get to define it, discover it, uniquely create it, and express it as you see fit. As you play with both your masculine and feminine aspects, you get to determine which expressions feel authentic to you and inspire the most pleasure.

In most traditions, feminine energy is receptive. It's no coincidence that orgasm is often paired with the term "coming." It's not something you can chase, but rather invite. If you want to be in love with your life, you have to make love to it. Open yourself to receiving and allow yourself to believe it. It will come. It will respond to your invitation, because when you invite and align yourself with open receiving, you become magnetic. You begin attracting. Don't want, don't force, don't chase–just believe that you are worthy of receiving everything. Let go of anything not in alignment with that.

I've never felt sexier than right after orgasm. It's transcendent. I experience time, life, and myself differently. I'm so deeply in my body, consumed in ecstasy, and I get a welcome break from being in my head and overthinking everything. It opens channels of feeling, intuiting, creating, and simply being. I am happier, healthier, and more productive, balanced, patient, loving, generous, and forgiving. In short, orgasms make me a better human. Something happens in my brain and body that enables me to feel and see myself differently. I feel completely at ease, like everything in the world is going to be okay.

Suddenly, like magic, I look at my body and feel not just tolerance, but true acceptance and gratitude for it. How could I be mad at something that allows me to experience so much beauty and pleasure? All of the things I usually criticize about my body seem so small now, so trivial. Sure, you could argue this may be the spike of dopamine and oxytocin in my brain and that signs of physical arousal align with classic definitions of beauty, but it's more than that. It's blissful, connected, radiant, and sensual. It feels like a beautiful truth in my body that challenges every shameful narrative about sexual pleasure. It cuts through all the socially conditioned bullshit messages and brings me right down to the embodied truth of who I am. I am love, beauty, creativity. I am juicy, overflowing with life and vibrancy.

Clearly, the result of my personal experiment with solo sexual exploration has been overwhelmingly positive. I've concluded that orgasms are the most extraordinary gift of this human experience. My orgasms have been the most empowering, healing, energizing, inspiring, and beautiful aspect of my life. They help me fulfill my life purpose and bring balance to the pain of this life experience. They are an embodiment of love, a prayer to the Divine, a sacred communion, and a spiritual devotion. Joyfully expressing through orgasm is a celebration of life and a pathway to creation and inspiration. This intimate connection with myself is a tool for healing and a powerful amplifying energy, as well as a practice of receiving pure pleasure and ecstasy and a way to have fun!

JOURNAL PRACTICE:

1. How might your own solo sex practice and/or orgasmic energy be healing for you?

2. What beliefs about your body, sexuality, pleasure, or yourself would you like to challenge and replace?

3. How might you practice inviting your own desire and arousal? What kinds of things excite your arousal and stoke the fire of your own sacred sexuality? Are there any aspects of yourself (fantasies, desires, or dynamics) that you would like to reclaim and reduce shame?

4. What leads you to soften, surrender, and open to more love in your life?

5. When you touch your body, how do you want to feel?

6. Our hands are an extension of our hearts. How can your hands be a tool for loving yourself more fully? For example, can you hold yourself, grasp your skin, and feel the lusciousness of the body you're in? Or perhaps it feels more authentic in this moment to place one hand on your heart and

the other on your stomach and breathe while holding yourself with loving presence. Consider journaling about an intention or practice you'd like to set or write about your experience doing this practice.

RESOURCES:

The following resources fill some of the holes that traditional sex education leaves untouched (*wink*):

If you are interested in exploring your own Erotic Blueprint layout, there is a low-cost online quiz you can take, paired with some additional information and resources to help you navigate your personal blueprint at https://theblueprintbreakthrough.com/.

If you struggle to achieve arousal, authentic desire, or orgasm–or if you'd simply like to deepen your relationship to your body, enhance your pleasure, and explore different ways to achieve orgasm–I'd highly recommend an incredible resource called BodySex, a practice developed by one of my personal heroes and female sexual pleasure pioneers, Betty Dodson, PhD. There is a website with incredibly useful articles, educational videos, podcasts, and events that are specifically created to help women connect with their bodies, heal, and increase pleasure. Check out https://dodsonandross.com/ and its sister site https://bodysex.com/. Betty wrote an article entitled "Learn a New Orgasm: How to Upgrade Your Masturbation Technique" in which she discusses her recommended masturbation technique as well as four different types of orgasms that she has categorized.

To explore more on shadow healing with fantasies and kinks, I'd recommend the book *Existential Kink: Unmask Your Shadow and Embrace Your Power (A method for getting what you want by getting off on what you don't)* by Carolyn Elliott.

SEXUAL MANIFESTING

For a long time, I didn't understand the concept of manifesting. There were times throughout my childhood that I would hear about the law of attraction or the power of positive thinking, and it seemed like nothing more than a social trend with no credibility. I watched as family members or friends would go through the motions and talk about how they were going to drastically change their life by telling themselves what they wanted to believe, but I wouldn't see anything change. So you can understand why I wasn't all that excited about this concept as a young adult. I had no interest in getting my hopes up and putting my energy into something that didn't work and only invited more disappointment into my life.

I have always believed in the power of positive thinking to the degree that the way we talk to ourselves and what we believe affects the way we feel and how we experience things. As I studied psychology, it was fascinating to see the transformational power of a reframe. Our experience really is defined by the way we look at things. It took much longer to recognize there is more to the story with the power of our beliefs. As I have gotten older, I have seen how self-doubt, shame, fear, and lack of commitment can get in the way of creating drastic shifts in our reality. The principle of manifesting is pretty simple, but the execution can be tricky. The process essentially involves creating a state of being and reinforcing it through consistency and repetition. The formula for this process includes imagery, emotion (or energy), thoughts or beliefs, and action.

In my experience, I have found that all of these components are required for being successful in getting the result I want. One of the key pieces I have noticed is related to my thoughts. It doesn't work as well if I simply repeat thoughts over and over again. I have to really invest in feeling them and *believing* them. Whether it be through faith or raw determination, I have to go all in with whatever I am choosing to believe. Otherwise, just going through the motions falls flat. This concept has been described as "playing full out," "going all in," or a historical reference of "burning the boats" to eliminate any alternatives to success.

I start with a vision of what I desire for myself. It might be related to a relationship, a feeling, my career, a goal, or a lifestyle. Then the tricky part–I fully commit. I choose to claim it and step into it by making it real. I hold myself accountable to any actions that would support this vision as if it were already true. I become it. This process has worked for me to set goals for myself and achieve them. I decide who I'm going to be and don't allow failure to be an option. This is where my stubborn personality, grit, and relentless determination have served me well (thank you, Capricorn stars).

While this version of goal setting and tenacity has served me well, it has required an incredible amount of energy, discipline, and time to achieve the goals I set for myself. It has helped me embrace the strengths of my masculine and I'm grateful for the fire I have cultivated through building my reality that way. Tony Robbins said that if you change your story, state, and strategy, then you change your life. I find his approach to these principles really valuable and also highly masculine. There is wisdom and validity in this application, as I have experienced in my masculine approach to goal setting. But I have experienced the most miraculous transformation when I apply these principles through my feminine.

Some of the gifts I associate with my feminine include creativity, expression, sensitivity, and intuition. As I have integrated these gifts and learned to apply them, it has changed the way I relate to my dreams and the process of creating. I have learned additional skills that have accelerated the process and pair extremely well with the tools I have already been practicing. When I create my life with the feminine, it comes from expression. I create the state mentally, emotionally, and physically. We have energy bodies and physical bodies, and both are required for manifesting. The body is the bridge and tool to turning our dreams into reality. This is where we apply our gifts of creativity and commune with God and the universe through our sensuality and sexuality. It is not about analyzing or doing, it is simply being and expressing the feeling from the body.

This process can be intuitive and come naturally as I envision my dreams that I am passionate about and feel excited to create. Other times, it can take some time to reflect and get clear on what I would like to call in. I love journaling as a practice to create a vision and describe it in detail so I can connect to the feeling. It requires presence and slowing down enough to connect with my imagination and creativity. Often, it is difficult to feel creative or inspired if I am in a stressed state, so I use movement, music, breath work, or meditation to clear my mind and manage my stress. Then I engage in something that helps me create a flow state, often through dance, singing, journaling, or stretching to get into my body. Then I create my vision, considering what it would look like and imagining what it would feel like. I allow myself to feel the emotion and pair it with a belief or affirmation that supports it, framed in the present tense (e.g., "I am abundant," "I am magnetic," "I am limitless").

Orgasmic energy is an amplifying power to this process. It's an embodiment of what I'm creating. When I add pleasure and power to that degree, it's the ultimate magnetism of the Divine Feminine. I am in a heightened, altered state of creativity. I can use this state for rewiring my beliefs, healing, alchemy, and manifesting dreams into reality. I make love to the visions of my dreams and imagine them already existing as truth. The practice is connecting with the feeling and embodying it with my pleasure. Then I follow it up with actions that reinforce it, which come much more naturally and easily when I have already created the state and am embodying joyful energy. This experience of sexual manifesting has brought magic to my life. I have used it to heal my heart and body and to support me in bringing my dreams to life. It may sound socially deviant, far-fetched, or crazy because of how far it is from the mainstream narrative about sexuality. I've decided I'm okay being sexually deviant and rebellious if it means deviating from shame, oppression, and distortions to truth, beauty, love, connection, and spiritual integration. The practice may look different from person to person, because it is an intuitive process through personal exploration. As I share this principle with other women, I love hearing about the variations in each individual experience.

EXERCISE AND JOURNAL PRACTICE:

Imagine something you want to feel. What would that feel like in your body? What action invites that feeling? How would you express that feeling? Think of it as role playing. Allow yourself to picture it, embody it, and express it as though it were real. Let yourself fully commit to it, uninhibited. Notice how you feel during and after the exercise, emotions, thoughts, and body sensations. Journal your experience.

THE BEST I'VE EVER HAD

The Divine is the greatest lover I have ever had. Playing with the energies of feminine and masculine within me and allowing my sensuality to include devotion and fantasy, intertwined with role playing and visualizing–this is sex magic, sacred sexuality, and sexual manifesting. For readers who have experienced fear conditioning with shame and secrecy around sexuality, this concept can be overwhelming. Replacing the traditional religious narrative that has always been taught can feel like blasphemy. But consider this–what if the discomfort you feel about making love with God is the same thing that prevents you from loving yourself and feeling loved? Think about it, if you have been taught that God does not approve of sexual behavior outside of procreation and that pleasure is selfish, carnal, and creates distance between you and God, you have been taught God will reject that aspect of your nature. As a result, you may have also learned to reject that aspect of your nature. Why were we designed with the incredible capacity for pleasure if not meant to enjoy it and use it in this life? Especially since the only function of the clitoris is pleasure! Perhaps there is a significant reason for this beyond procreation. Procreation could certainly be achieved without pleasure. In fact, if you ask a large percentage of women, I bet they would agree they did not get their children through an experience of ecstasy.

The Divine always offers love and support on our path. Prayer is not just a matter of asking for support, but also believing and being willing to receive it. You can experience this for yourself by asking the Divine to enter you–to come into your life and become your lover. Any stigma or conditioning that causes you to recoil at that idea is a byproduct of purity culture. Why would we not want to make love to the Divine? Why would we not want the Divine to be an integral part of our intimacy and pleasure?

There are infinite ways Divine energies can serve me by shaping and expanding my spiritual identity. I invite them into my world as I engage in a process of creativity and expression. The practice of sacred sexuality is a collaboration of imagery, sensations, and intentions as I embody the essence of all that is me, interconnected with everyone and everything.

To make this a bit more concrete, imagine you are role playing in a fantasy. You play the role of a woman who you want to be–whatever version of yourself you'd like to embody. Begin to imagine what it would be like if you were already there. My favorite is a woman who is empowered, loved, and unconditionally worthy. What would it feel like to be the woman worthy of receiving so much love, adoration, pleasure, acceptance, and compassion, and being deeply known, seen, and cherished? To feel at ease with yourself, confident in who you are, trusting yourself and your gifts, speaking your truth, sharing your passion, and feeling comfortable in your own skin. To be fully seen, witnessed, and expressed in the fullness of who you are with forgiveness and grace for your mistakes. If you were unconditionally loved, how would you treat yourself? How would you touch your body? Can you imagine it? Really visualize and feel it. Now imagine being the lover of this woman. How beautiful is she in your eyes? How would you speak to her, caress her, hold her, protect her, serve her, indulge her, honor her, love her? If you really saw all of who she is in her unique divine essence, how would you treat her? What would you be willing to do for her? How would you respond to her imperfections, mistakes, and idiosyncrasies?

What if the true nature of our being is to love and be loved like this? What if the truth of who we are is discovered and experienced in these sacred spaces and intimate moments between lovers? What if you didn't have to wait for the right partner to experience it? Could you allow yourself to invite the Divine into your sacred solo sex practice? Could you be open to receiving love like this, through you, from a higher power consciousness? You can choose to allow Divine Feminine energy to flow through you as you soften into your sensuality, creativity, sweet tenderness, and open yourself to receive. This also includes the full range of untamed emotions, allowing them to be felt and expressed through your body. Unleash the passion and embrace all of your emotionality. Use your movement, touch, sound, vibration, smell, taste, and intuition to lead you through sensual pleasure exploration. Lose yourself in the sensation, expression, and embodiment of being. It doesn't have a right or wrong way to it, just your truth in each moment. If it feels good, let your body do it. Once connected, feeling juicy and overflowing, you can choose to stay here and play as long as you'd like, basking in the deliciousness of the feminine. Or you can invite the Divine Masculine to join.

How would it feel to make love with the Divine Masculine? How would you invite it? Imagine surrendering your body, softening your heart, and breathing Divine Love into your yoni. Draw it in with your pelvic floor muscle, up your spine through the crown of your head, and back down your front as you exhale and relax, then begin again. As you do this, stimulate your clitoris and visualize the energy you are inviting in. What would it be like to receive that much unconditional love and presence? Can you imagine being

139

penetrated by the essence of God in the form of Divine Masculine? Could you allow yourself to take it in? As you channel and embody the Divine Feminine, could you surrender your heart, mind, body, and spirit in devotion to love? Loving yourself, being loved, loving God, loving others, being love. If the pleasure of your lovemaking, the power of your orgasm, and the passion of your soul could be devoted to something, what would it be? What are the deepest desires of your heart? Imagine what it would be like to have them filled. Imagine the best lover you've never had. This is the realm where anything is possible. God is infinite and the depth of love is inconceivable. Our imagination is the only limit.

Being my own lover and making love with the Divine has been an incredibly sacred experience. It has taken many forms, just as prayers take many forms throughout our lives. My sacred sexual practice of making love has been profoundly transformational in my connection with God and becoming one with love. I experience it very similarly to a deep meditation as I am in sync with my body and present in each moment. It is much like an organic, intuitive dance with my physical, emotional, and energetic state. In this practice, I trust my heart, mind, body, and spirit to create the experience that will benefit my highest good. I've experienced deep meditative visions, colors, and states of euphoria as I invite the Divine to be a part of my practice and dedicate my orgasms to love and healing.

This chapter is short and sweet, but it is the heart and soul of this book. I cannot describe to you the beauty I have experienced through this practice. It is only something you can come to know for yourself. It is sacred, precious, and life-changing. I pray that everyone experiences the truth of what is possible through sacred sexuality in their own way.

JOURNAL PRACTICE:

In addition to the prompts provided throughout the chapter, consider the following:

1. How do you feel about the idea of making love to the Divine?

2. How might your view/experience of sexuality shift if you include it as spiritual practice?

HANDS-ON EXPERIENCE:

The best way to learn is through experience. I invite you to explore your own solo sex practice as an opportunity to collaborate with the Divine. Consider what your own version of sacred sexuality could look like and what kind of prayer you might embody to invite the Divine in. I recommend setting boundaries for yourself and inviting only loving energy that is in service of your highest good through the power of unconditional love. You have the power to choose who and what to open your heart, mind, body, and spirit to. In my experience, there is nothing more powerful than unconditional Divine Love. I feel safe in my practice and in my vulnerability when I set my intentions in this way.

PART THREE

SEXUALITY BETWEEN

It's no secret that relationships come with more complexities than being alone. They also come with incredible opportunities for healing, expansion, connection, learning, growing, and creating. I think Esther Perel put it perfectly when she said, "The quality of our relationships determines the quality of our lives."

AUTHENTIC RELATING
& RADICAL RESPONSIBILITY

When I think about relationships with others, I can't help but start with understanding my own identity. As I have grown older and gained more experience with relationships, it's more apparent than ever that relationships serve as mirrors. For me to discuss the truths I've discovered about sacred sexuality between myself and another, I have to talk about what it means to show up authentically in relationships. Brené Brown teaches us that authenticity can't exist without vulnerability. It also requires critical self-awareness and personal accountability. When I didn't know who I was, I was mostly living as a product of my environment and conditioning while growing up. I wasn't fully aware of how my trauma had affected me, so I wasn't fully aware of the wounds I was projecting or the unconscious patterns and defense mechanisms I was exhibiting. My lack of awareness of these things was a large factor in perpetuating my own suffering. The first step toward authentic relating was realizing the difference between who I authentically was and who I was socialized or taught to be. The next step was taking radical responsibility for the ways I was acting that weren't serving me and aligning my actions with my own integrity.

As I've reflected on my relationship history, I've recognized things I thought I knew, things I knew all along, and things I didn't have any clue about. I used to think I knew what I wanted in a relationship. I knew I wanted something strong and healthy with mutual love and respect, but I didn't know what that looked like. My education about relationships started as early as I can remember. My childhood was filled with dysfunction and I didn't have many, if any, examples of healthy relationships in my family. Throughout my childhood, I was often put in the middle of parental disputes over custody issues, power struggles, passive aggressive manipulation, and parents bad mouthing each other. I was a middle child, third from the bottom of a large blended family that was split between both households. Despite all those people, I remember often feeling isolated, misunderstood, and lonely. Internally, I was on the defense, constantly anticipating others' reactivity. I got really good at reading social cues and adapting to keep the peace.

While both households were conservative, both sets of parents had a different parenting style. My primary home was a lot stricter and controlling while the other was a bit more lenient and gave me autonomy. I had complicated relationships with both of my step-parents who were dominant personalities in each home. The combination of a conservative upbringing from both sides and a predominantly strict environment made it difficult for me to feel truly seen.

As a teenager, impulsivity was like a pressure release. I would take advantage of the autonomy at the other house because I felt like I could finally breathe. This dynamic didn't help my experience of pendulum swinging as I was living in a landscape of extremes. It became a kind of dance–keep it in control, act out, feel shame, repent, rinse and repeat. I associated control with safety and predictability. But it was also suffocating. Sometimes I felt peace when I was doing what I thought was "the right thing." I connected deeply to God and had close friends who would stay up all night with me discussing the meaning of life and philosophy. But when I was living this extreme polarized life, I was rejecting half of my personality and I wasn't truly happy.

Despite occasionally feeling calm and satisfied with my self-righteousness and perfectionism-driven accomplishments, it was mostly in my impulsive "fuck it" moments that I truly felt carefree pleasure and joy. My conditioning caused me to feel great shame about these indulgent moments because it was against the rules that I had internalized and my inner critic was rather effective at keeping me in check. The story I told myself about my identity–that I was unworthy and something was inherently wrong with me–caused deep-seated shame. I was taught that complying and living according to "the plan of happiness" that my religion had prescribed would make me happy. But when I had my faith crisis, or what I like to call my Spiritual Awakening, I took my first step in the right direction.

Because I had gotten confused and disconnected from myself at a very young age, I didn't realize I had lost myself. My faith crisis was the catalyst for finding myself again. It was the beginning of The Great Unraveling of who I was taught to be to make room for who I was always meant to be, born to be, and authentically becoming. It's ironic that as I began rediscovering my authenticity in my early twenties, everyone in my community perceived me as getting lost. I was the lost sheep, the wanderer, the apostate, and the rebel. But the real problem was not that I had lost faith in my religion, but that along the way I had lost faith in myself. Somehow, as a child I had been convinced that I couldn't trust myself and believed the reason I felt like I didn't fit in or belong was because of me. If I could only change myself, become perfect enough, follow the plan of happiness just precisely enough, or be obedient and righteous enough, I would be worthy. I had been taught to be what everyone else needed or wanted me to be to keep the peace. I did this not only because of my social conditioning and the influence of religion and the patriarchy, but also as a trauma response to a chaotic and unsafe environment. I coped with the unpredictability around me by gaining control through perfectionism and complying. I was a rule follower to my core–at school, at home, in society. It wasn't long until the fire of my inner rebel started showing. When I wasn't able to express the true aspects of myself, they showed up rebelliously.

As I entered my teens, I became more independent, outspoken, and stubborn. I often asserted my autonomy in covert ways, careful to avoid conflict when possible. Other times, I'd pick the battles worth fighting for and push back with my strong will. I stood up for myself when I felt I was being treated unfairly, although it took quite a toll on my nervous system to do so. Romantic relationships in my teens were toxic and immature with high conflict, a lack of boundaries, and volatility. They often alternated between intense fighting and passionate repairing.

As I transitioned to college, I was eager to solve the mystery and understand what a healthy, functional relationship could be. I was well aware of what I didn't want, but I thought if I could understand functional relationships logically, I would be able to create it for myself. My education served me very well in understanding myself and my relationship patterns, as well as those of my family. It helped me understand and organize a lot of my early experiences and validated that I wasn't crazy. I learned that I had a fair amount of anxious attachment tendencies due to the inconsistency I experienced from my young, under-resourced parents who had a high-conflict marriage, divorce, and co-parenting.

As I examined my upbringing, I realized that the greatest areas of rebellion and shame were wrapped around my sexuality and body.

These were the aspects of self-expression that were stifled and policed the most. I wanted to wear what made me feel confident, empowered, sexy, and free. I wanted to connect with others, explore, play, and embrace my sensuality. As a teenager, my sensitivity, tender heart, passionate fire, desire for deep connection, and need for emotional release all channeled into my developing sexuality. It was against the rules to embrace it, even if I loved my boyfriends and felt deeply connected to them. Even more out of the question was exploring my bisexual curiosities. I barely let myself go there in the socially acceptable context of truth or dare, and even then, it was only kissing. The cycle of pressure buildup and impulsivity followed by devastating shame spiraling and repenting continued through the time I started dating the man I ended up marrying.

Dating him was a fresh opportunity to practice abstinence and, of course, he would help me because he was the first boy that I dated who shared my religious beliefs and was just as committed to being "worthy." Not only that, but he knew my past and was willing to accept me, even with my history of sexual promiscuity. He was safe, devoted, faithful, and loving. Eleven months after our first date, we were married. I was twenty. The joke was on me because by waiting, neither of us had any way of learning about our sexual incompatibility until we were already married. But that was just the tip of the iceberg, because only two years later, my faith crisis began and my identity started unraveling.

Over several years together, we grew, made mistakes, and went through a lot of messy things. We struggled with our sexual compatibility from the beginning, as well as our communication and emotional intimacy. We each went through a faith crisis separately, at different times and in different ways. It was incredibly lonely for me because I started transitioning two years before he was ready to confront his own questioning. I was suffering through the hardest thing I had ever been through and I couldn't talk to my partner about it. The person who had become my safe place, who I had built a stable home with, was no longer a safe place when it came to this. The stability of the relationship and future we had envisioned together were being threatened by the changes I was going through. During those two years, my only support came from Facebook groups that my sister-in-law had introduced me to. She also later introduced me to women's retreats that were vital in my healing journey. I will forever be grateful for her and the life preservers she threw to me when I felt like I was drowning.

Things got a bit better once my husband and I were both able to share our experiences with identity and existential questions. We were able to talk more openly, but we still struggled immensely to communicate effectively. It was deeply painful and challenging to navigate all the pieces that were shifting and the ways it was calling our compatibility into question even more intensely. I was trying to fit this new version of myself into something I had chosen from one of my extremes–a checklist of priorities that no longer represented my authenticity. How could I consciously choose someone to marry if I didn't even know the real me? For a long time, I wasn't ready to face what it could mean. I had never considered divorce as an option, especially after what I went through growing up. I tried fixing it, changing myself, and forcing it to fit. All of my shadows came out to play as I avoided the truth of what I was really feeling. I'm not proud of the choices I made while I was in so much pain. I hurt him and he hurt me. We went to counseling and developed tools to communicate a lot more effectively. After five years of marriage, we lovingly parted ways. To this day, he is a beautiful human that I love deeply and I know he cares about me. I'm deeply grateful for everything we taught each other and the part it played in bringing me to where I am today.

Due to getting married so young, I had moved in with my husband from living with my parents, so I had no idea what it was like to live alone and free–to support myself, make my own rules, and exist independently. As a single woman, I was excited to explore my sexuality. I wanted to date and play and explore this new version of myself without guilt or shame or acting outside of my integrity. I don't think I realized how complex the process of healing was and how deeply my wounds had been affecting me. The pattern of extremes continued in my dating life as I attracted partners who were emotionally unavailable but exciting and sexy or partners who were sensitive, kind, and sweet but lacked the passion of polarity.

My anxious attachment style came with a deep unconscious story that I was too much, not enough, and, at the root of it, unworthy. I began to see how this story was affecting every aspect of my being. From my work to my habits, my relationships, my pleasure–everything.

I had been doing my healing work for a while now and was aware of this distorted belief to a degree. What I didn't realize was that I was still seeking the solution from everywhere *except* inside of me. This is a process I now refer to as "emotional outsourcing." I was seeking validation from external sources and my wounds were unconsciously attracting experiences I didn't want but were ultimately serving me. Based on what I was projecting, I was attracting a reflective experience for what I needed to see. This was not a comfortable truth to realize through a series of heartbreaks and relationships but they all taught me something unique. I didn't realize that all along I had been dating various aspects of me–triggers that needed triggering and showing me parts that still needed healing, all different variations of the same thing. I was learning how to love myself and that all of my unmet needs were my responsibility.

To say my needs are my responsibility doesn't mean I have to do it alone or that I am not supported–I've had everything I needed the whole time. I was missing the perspective and ability to see that life is always happening for me, but I have to let it happen. I was missing the tools and awareness of how to take personal responsibility for my experience to create my own reality. Now that I have learned to look through that lens, I am always asking the questions, "What is the lesson?" and "Where is the gift in this experience?" If the answer is not clear immediately, I trust that the clarity will come. It always does.

My wounds were attracting those experiences to help me see them and heal them. Every single one was an opportunity that has made me stronger, more loving, resilient, fiery, trusting, and surrendered, even if it takes a while to get there. A wise friend once told me, "If not this, then something better." There has been medicine in this phrase as I remind myself of it whenever my life does not go as I expect it to. It offers comfort and reassurance when I go into fearful patterns or my attachment wounds want to revert to clinging or controlling.

As I have learned to cope more effectively with uncertainty, I have learned to embrace the present moment and enjoy the journey of this life unfolding. I am an active participant in creating my life with dreaming, manifesting, and action accountability, but there are absolutely pieces I am better off surrendering. I have discovered many hidden lessons and gifts in my previous relationships that ended, especially when I thought I knew what I wanted and who I wanted to be with. There have been relationships in the past that I desperately wanted to work. I was still operating out of a lens of wanting to be chosen by those partners. But the emotionally unavailable men I thought I was so in love with were really just reflections of my own longing to be loved. Them choosing me would not give me the satisfaction I craved so deeply. It was more about being chosen and feeling good enough than anything specific about them. A game changing question became, "Instead of trying to be chosen, why am I really choosing them?" I put many men on pedestals and allowed myself to feel small, getting caught in patterns of changing myself or proving my lovability in an effort to achieve validation. So much of this was unconscious and I truly didn't see it.

The medicine for an insecure attachment style is having corrective experiences. This is only possible through practicing being in the context of relationships and navigating the messy parts with as much vulnerability, accountability, and compassion as possible. I used to feel ashamed of my anxiety in relationships. I blamed myself for having insecurities and thought they made me less loveable, so I'd try to hide them and pretend to have it all together. I used to believe the myth that I needed to change myself to be secure enough to deserve a healthy, loving relationship. If I could just control my emotions, hide my insecurity, and manage myself well enough, I would have the love I was craving. Even after I started my healing journey, I struggled with shame for my insecure attachment tendencies and thought I needed to be all healed and "healthy" before being worthy of a loving relationship. These patterns of perfectionism were not serving me. In fact, they were creating a barrier to my healing because they were reinforcing the idea that I am not already worthy of love exactly as I am.

Another pattern I would often get stuck in was trying to change my partners and criticizing them for not meeting my needs. I would blame them and feel angry or resentful for their emotional unavailability. Again, this was not about them. After all, I had chosen them! What I was really doing was giving away my power by not taking personal accountability for my own emotional needs.

I wasn't clearly communicating when I was feeling insecure but was demanding instead. I told myself I was doing my part by communicating, but I wasn't truly being vulnerable and asking for emotional reassurances. I was telling them the ways they needed to be more open, more expressive, more assertive, or more of whatever I was wanting. Those were the "needs" I was communicating. Meanwhile, I was neglecting my own vulnerability in my controlling tendencies of perfectionism, trying to be a perfect, confident, lovable, fun, generous, compassionate partner.

On the outside I presented as someone who takes accountability and is always seeking to improve themselves. I was doing my best to be the best self, friend, partner, and professional that I could be. I would focus my energy and attention outside of myself on my partner, friends, or others and would not spend nearly enough time just sitting down with myself to *feel my feelings*. I had to learn to hold space for them, ask them what they were needing, and give them love, acceptance, presence, patience, and understanding. I was obsessed with self-awareness (the irony isn't lost on me) and was critical of others' lack of vulnerability (again, irony) when I was still avoiding the most vulnerable parts of me. I was neglecting the parts of me that felt unworthy, unlovable, scared, hurt, ashamed, and unwanted (especially by me). I was not prioritizing my own happiness, doing hobbies that brought me joy, or allowing full expression, which stifles creativity. So, I was working, working, working, and finding no relief.

This pattern only expressed further in my sexuality. I wanted to feel fulfilled, inspired, desired, playful, and free. My arousal was dependent on my partners initiating me in just the right way. It was a box I unintentionally put them and myself in. I looked to my partners to fulfill this need because I didn't know how to make myself happy. My solo sex practice was not inspiring. I wasn't taking the time to explore my own desires other than what I wanted my partner to do to me, then getting frustrated when I didn't have a partner who was able or willing to be what I needed them to be. I didn't know how to cultivate my own arousal, how to fully express my desires, or how to create my own pleasure. I was making them responsible for my sexual satisfaction from start to finish. How unsexy is that for either of us? Sex is where adults get to play. When it feels like a responsibility, expectation, chore, or demand on either end, the fun goes away. There is no room for spontaneity, creativity, or exploration and there is no room for the fire of desire to breathe, burn, anticipate. Novelty, variety, and creativity are essential ingredients for play. When we apply pressure, it becomes suffocating. Of course, sex is complex and there are many variables involved so this is merely one dimension of truth I have discovered through my experience.

I give myself a ton of grace and compassion for the patterns of my past. I know I didn't do any of it intentionally–I just wasn't taught anything different. I know in my heart that I don't want to be critical, selfish, or hurtful toward anyone, especially not people I love so deeply. It's painful to realize my patterns were causing pain not only for me, but for the partners who were genuinely trying their best to love me. That's not to say they were perfect and didn't have their own shortcomings. My feelings were valid, but I also made mistakes and I have absolute accountability in the fact that I was a co-creator of my own suffering. I share this so candidly because, although painful and uncomfortable to realize the truth, as the old saying goes, telling the truth really did set me free. Reclaiming personal power is synonymous with taking accountability and responsibility for my own happiness. What I choose to believe, how I get my needs met, how I show up, what I give, and how open I am to receive are all tools that empower me to be happy and free.

It wasn't until I acknowledged my codependency that I was really able to take responsibility for the underlying needs that were causing it. It has been only through vulnerability and embracing my deepest insecurities with love and compassion that I have found love beyond what I could have ever imagined. I started within myself and practiced allowing it in from outside of myself. Now I practice giving my inner child what she always needed–acceptance, unconditional love, being seen, valued, and heard. I remind her, frequently, that she is not too needy, too sensitive, too vulnerable, too much, or not enough of anything. She is loved exactly as she is. This changed the way I show up in relationship with myself and, by extension, with my partners.

By taking radical responsibility for myself and my healing, I was able to start feeling my deep, uncomfortable feelings. It was vulnerable, scary, and incredibly liberating and empowering. This is where I was able to heal my wounds around sexuality too. It wasn't through finding a lover who knew just how to touch me or how to initiate in the way I wanted them to. It was through acknowledging the shame, discomfort, and lack of familiarity with touching my own body in a way that was fulfilling. I had explored solo sex, but it felt unfulfilling and shallow and uninspired. I desired to be loved, desired, and met by a conscious partner. I didn't just desire orgasm, I wanted connection, intimacy, and depth. I didn't know how to get this on my own, until I learned about the concept of polarity and sacred union, within and between. I had to learn how to be both. And I had to learn how to drop into my feminine *desire* for the masculine to penetrate me. And most significantly, I had to invite the Divine and nurture my inner divinity through my sexuality.

I can now practice surrendering control and releasing expectations so I can be open to the Divine giving me what I need instead of what I think I want. I can express my dreams and desires and trust that I can have them, even if it looks different than I originally imagine. Because, "If not this, then something better." When I surrender trying to force my life to look a certain way and focus more on feelings, visions, and dreams, and take responsibility for how I respond to what life gives me, the result comes out more beautifully than I could ever picture on my own. When I practice living in the present and letting life love me, wherever I am and whoever I am with offers an opportunity to practice loving and being loved. Every experience can serve my highest good and growth.

JOURNAL PRACTICE:

1. What is your relationship with vulnerability? How do you identify, express, and cope with vulnerable emotions in the context of your relationships? How does this impact you and/or your relationships? Where did you learn this strategy? Is there anything you would like to change?

2. Why do you want to connect to your pleasure, sensuality, and sexual desire? In other words, what's in it for you? Having connection to this can be a great place to build self-accountability and ownership of your sexuality in your relationship(s).

3. How can you take more responsibility for your own pleasure, satisfaction, arousal, desire (e.g., communication of desires and needs, self-care, solo sex, or cultivating more passion in your own life)?

RESOURCES:

For more information on authentic relating, vulnerability, and overcoming shame, I highly recommend the following books:

- *The Gifts of Imperfection* by Brené Brown (and/or any of her books, her TED talk called "The Power of Vulnerability," or her Netflix special called *The Call to Courage*)

- *Untamed* by Glennon Doyle

INTEGRITY &
ACCOUNTABILITY

There's a principle in social psychology called the law of reciprocity, which I believe is applicable within intimacy. The theory suggests that when someone does something kind with genuine intention, it generally has an effect of creating a natural desire to reciprocate. It's a wonderful concept in theory, and has validity in many cases, but I'll admit it can be a bit idealist. I'd like to believe relationships and life were as simple as this, but in my experience, I have learned there are nuances and complexities to relationships. I still believe in the spirit of this message and have witnessed the magic that is possible when this dynamic is at its best. When I respect someone's boundaries or show consideration, it is likely they will respect mine in return. When I give love and support generously, it's naturally easier for my partner to reciprocate. The best relationships I've experienced have involved a give-give dynamic, with both people being generous and considerate, being open to receiving, asking for support, setting boundaries, and expressing gratitude and appreciation.

On the other side of the coin, I've experienced dynamics of over-giving or being taken for granted, exploited, and deceived. When I give without setting boundaries, it is disempowering and creates a susceptibility for being taken advantage of. I've also experienced my own shadows with this dynamic, being capable of manipulation, passive aggression, entitlement, blaming, victimhood, and resentment. I believe the key to reciprocity being able to thrive in any relationship is to release expectations, set boundaries, and take responsibility for my experience with personal accountability and integrity.

It doesn't serve me to try and force, control, or manipulate my partner into doing what I want them to do (i.e., "if I do this, they should do that"). It is much more effective to put my energy into what I am giving to the relationship. I can choose to do my part in creating a culture of gratitude and appreciation (instead of entitlement or expectation), mutual respect and consideration, and taking turns giving and receiving (without scorekeeping). I can choose to make requests rather than demands, express my vulnerable feelings and needs instead of criticizing, manage my own reactivity, and take accountability for my impact in the relationship. Owning my impact includes being mindful of how I am responding to my partner's needs, how I am creating space for them to be seen, and *being* the partner I would want to be with. If I am doing everything I can to show up in the relationship with as much accountability as I can, I am much more capable of discerning whether there is enough balanced reciprocity to continue investing my energy to the same degree.

What I have learned, and am still learning, is what it means to practice this concept with integrity. I do my best to give generously with sincerity and without ulterior motive, expectation, or manipulation. I try to align my actions with the intention in my heart and live according to my values. I practice the golden rule to treat others how I would like to be treated. I focus on my own accountability and the ways I am expressing myself or responding to others from a place of authenticity. I try to be true to my word and follow through on my commitments. I try to own when I am feeling reactive or defensive and take ownership for the impact of my actions and choices. I try to cultivate genuine empathy and compassion before responding to my partner, and make it safe for my partner to be vulnerable with me. I take responsibility for communicating my expectations, needs, and boundaries clearly and specifically to my partner or others. When I am hurt or upset, I do my best not to project, blame, or deny my role in conflicts. When my partner is hurt or upset, I do my best to understand, offer support, and own any contributions I made to their pain.

I am responsible for setting, reinforcing, and respecting my own boundaries, which includes recognizing the things I am choosing to do, invest, allow, or neglect. It also includes paying attention to how I am being treated and allowing it to inform my boundaries, adjusting them as needed. I respect the boundaries of others and don't project or pressure what I think they should be. I let go of trying to control others with my actions or trying to get a reaction. I cannot control or manipulate my partner with my own sexual behavior or influence on my partner's desire and arousal to achieve the type of intimate connection I desire. I don't close off or withhold love as a punishment and I choose to be open-hearted to the best of my ability in each moment. If my heart feels closed or guarded, I do what I need to regulate myself, communicate about what I am feeling, and ask for help with softening to reopen again. If there is such a thing as "the power of the least invested," I don't want it. Pride has no place in relationships if my ultimate goal is healthy love and intimate connection. As for my boundaries with reciprocity, I choose to invest my energy in a way that aligns with my values and integrity and trust my partner to do the same. I trust myself to set boundaries as I need to and take accountability for my part in creating the power couple dynamic I desire with a partner who is mutually invested.

It all sounds great, right? I will be the first to admit I don't do any of these things perfectly. I'm very capable of doing the very opposite of what I intend, which is why it takes practice to live with integrity. All of these are practices that I am learning from every day with valuable lessons as I make mistakes. They represent the values that I am devoted to as I try to live heart first and stay open to love.

These principles serve me in creating healthy relationships of any kind. In a romantic relationship, it sets a foundation of values that impact every aspect of connection, including sexual intimacy. When I apply the same tools to my sexuality in partnership, I get to take full responsibility for my own experience. It is not my partner's job to arouse me. It is not my partner's job to sexually satisfy me. It is not my partner's job to read my mind, to always know what I need, to define my boundaries, to convince me to value sexuality, or to define my sexual identity. All of these things are my responsibility to identify, understand, communicate, and engage in. Sexual intimacy in relationship is all about co-creation. It is an intimate connection with a shared interest. It's also not my responsibility to manage any of these things for my partner. My partner's sexual satisfaction is NOT my responsibility. Of course, I desire to give my partner pleasure and get joy from satisfying them, but there's an important distinction between what I authentically desire, and what is my responsibility.

With that being said, if I am completely closed off to my own sexuality, that will have an impact on my partner and the relationship. The goal is to create common interest, shared desires, and mutual respect of boundaries. If I am not investing in my own sexuality, I'm more prone to falling into patterns of people-pleasing or avoiding it entirely. This creates an imbalance in the relationship with my partner being the only one reaching to cultivate sexual intimacy, making it much less likely or even impossible to be

161

mutually satisfying. When my heart is open, I have a natural desire to connect with my partner and co-create mutual pleasure. When I invest in my own sexual identity, arousal, desire, and in the intimate connection with my partner both emotionally and physically, I am much more likely to experience the same from my partner and enjoy the benefits of intimacy that we create together. It is in this way that the law of reciprocity can serve as a formula for abundance in the relationship. We both get what we put in if my partner and I are both invested in exploring and creating a vibrant, fulfilling, expansive sex life, *and* we practice engaging with personal accountability and integrity to grow together through co-created intimacy.

JOURNAL PRACTICE:

What are the values you would like to hold yourself accountable for in your relationships? What would it look like to become the partner you desire to be with?

BOUNDARIES & CONSENT

Whether I am opening myself up energetically, spiritually, or physically to something outside of myself, boundaries and consent are absolutely necessary. It is my responsibility to keep myself safe and take accountability for what I am inviting into my body. My body is precious to me. If I love myself, I must protect my vulnerability and be willing to set the boundaries that are safe for me. Boundaries aren't only about safety, but they are also a standard of living. I am committed to not self-abandoning and I only choose things that are in alignment with my authenticity.

Part of this practice is releasing patterns of people-pleasing, over-giving, and peacekeeping. I must value my internal peace, my inner child, and my health and well-being enough to make myself a priority. To do this, I had to overcome the narrative that putting myself first is selfish. This is a common misconception that stems from a fear that caring about my own happiness means I won't care about the happiness of others. What if an authentic part of who I am feels joy in helping others? What if my core values include service, generosity, compassion, and meaningful sacrifice for people I love and things I believe in? I can trust myself enough to know that when I honor my boundaries and prioritize my own needs, the rest will happen naturally. I don't need to neglect myself or be self*less* to be considerate and loving. In fact, when I abandon myself and say yes to things I really don't want to do, it not only hurts me but it isn't kind to those I'm trying to serve. What if the most compassionate thing I can do for others is to honor my own needs? When I don't respect my own boundaries out of obligation, over-extending, or avoiding conflict, it leads to resentment, irritability, burnout, stress, and fatigue.

Here's a helpful exercise. Consider someone you love deeply. Would you want them to compromise their own boundaries to meet your needs? Would it feel good knowing they are only doing it because they feel obligated to? Would you want them to be intimate with you if you knew they really didn't want to? Have you ever had someone bring up a time they did something nice for you but it was laced with resentment? None of these things feel good. In my experience, I feel so much safer, loved, and secure in my relationships when we both express and respect our boundaries. If I trust that my partner will be honest with themselves and me about their boundaries, I feel much more at ease making requests, expressing desires, receiving love and acts of kindness, and showing up authentically. I won't carry anxiety about unspoken tension, resentment, passive aggression, emotional injuries, blaming, or toxicity growing in the relationship because we are both taking accountability for ourselves and our boundaries.

I would like to clarify that boundaries are different from sacrifice or compromise in relationships. We all have growth edges outside our comfort zones that we willingly lean into for the sake of bettering ourselves. We all make choices in relationships that include efforts to stretch toward our partner or make compromises as a team. Loving someone can often involve making personal sacrifices in service of another. These are beautiful values that can enrich intimacy and deepen love as long as they are done with integrity. If the sacrifice or compromise is within your boundaries, you're golden. I'm specifically referring to a common pattern that exists, especially among women, of saying yes when you would rather say no. As well intentioned as it may be, as conditioned as it may be, this pattern can be a huge risk for disconnecting from your power, pleasure, safety, sovereignty, joy, and overall well-being. At the beginning of our relationship, my partner told me, "If I haven't heard your no, I can't trust your yes." And y'all, let me tell you, that was the sexiest thing.

What does this have to do with sexuality? Everything. In the same way that foreplay begins outside the bedroom, so does setting boundaries and communicating. These patterns will follow you into your sexual play and may even be amplified because of the degree of vulnerability at stake. I had to learn to practice my no in every capacity when I became aware of my own tendencies like tolerating unwanted touch, expending excessive energy, over-giving, and allowing people, patterns, or things in my life that did not align for me. I had many sexual experiences of bypassing my own needs and desires to ensure my partners got what they needed. I would rush through foreplay, afraid of taking too long, and often allowed penetration before my body was ready. I would play along with my partner's desires, fantasies, or ways of touching me even when it was uncomfortable or painful for me. I let sexual encounters go on much longer than I wanted because I didn't want to disappoint them or seem like a tease. When it was too uncomfortable to say no after I had already said yes, I would allow it to continue with a "get it over with" mentality. I was caretaking everyone but me. My solo sex practice was non-existent or uninspiring. I was not in touch with my own pleasure and I wasn't cultivating my own desire, so I couldn't communicate what I wanted or needed. I wasn't attuned to my own body, and even when it was telling me what it needed, I wasn't listening or responding. I was critical of my partners and irritated when I was unsatisfied with our sex life. I blamed them when a major part of the problem was me.

Since becoming more aware of these tendencies, I've learned to listen to and trust my body to set my boundaries in sex and in anything. If it's not a clear YES, then it's a no or a maybe–with a pause for investigating. When I follow my yes, it keeps me safe and brings me pleasure, arousal, joy, and rich, authentic intimacy. My life is more inspiring and balanced, my relationships are healthier and more fulfilling, and my body is energetic, juicy, and deeply satisfied. My sensuality and the way I experience life is at its best when it is not dulled by burnout, exhaustion, dissociation, numbing, or living in a chronic state of stress. Stress is part of life and there are many things I don't have control over, but when I took control of setting my boundaries in every capacity, my life completely changed. I got really comfortable with saying no to others and saying yes to me. I would only say yes to others if it was also a yes to me, my body, and my capacity.

In the relationship with my body, I've become a no to any narrative that shames or claims my body needs to change to be considered beautiful, desirable, and worthy of love. I am a no to social situations or people that would perpetuate these messages. I express my truth, speak my boundaries, and remove myself from situations if necessary. I've become a no to any situation that would require me to dismiss something I'm feeling, bypass my authenticity, or numb myself to endure it (only to deal with the consequences later). If I am not comfortable with something, I don't do it. I've become a no to anyone who doesn't respect my no.

In my relationships with others, I listen to my body to discern the people I choose to have around me. This includes work and personal life settings. A mentor of mine used to define trust as a spectrum with degrees of safety and discerning who to trust, with what, and to what degree. I let my body govern where the boundaries need to be. There is a hidden wisdom, an intuition, and a sixth sense that I have learned to trust completely. My yoni is the most precious part of me. It is my sacred temple, the heart of my vulnerability. If my body doesn't give me the green light, I don't go there. If I get a green light that turns yellow, I pause and wait for clarity, then realign with whatever is green. If I get a red light, I respect the fuck out of it and stop to set the boundary. It is a constant practice with everyone, everything, every day.

JOURNAL PRACTICE:

1. What are you becoming a no to?

    Recognizing and honoring my no has created room for my YES. I am a yes to loving my body every day with radical acceptance of all its fluctuations and forms. I am a yes to celebrating my sensuality and pleasure by nurturing it every day and making my joy a priority. I am a yes to looking at myself in the mirror and admiring what I like about my body and replacing any critical thought with appreciation, compassion, and truth. I'm a yes to giving back to my body, tuning in and listening to what it needs, and nurturing it with gratitude for all that it does for me. I'm a yes for touching myself with loving hands, holding myself, caressing myself, and creating pleasure and ecstasy for myself. I am a yes to work that feels inspiring and fulfilling with purpose and meaning. I am a yes to relationships that are give and take with mutual respect and boundaries. I am a yes to putting myself first and cultivating my independence and sovereignty. I am a yes to asking for help, creating community, connection, and intimacy, and being open to giving and receiving love and support. I am a yes to creativity and authentic expression. I am a yes to living freely with choice, accountability, and integrity.

I am a yes to spiritual practices and energies that feed my soul, uplift me, and serve my highest good. I am a yes to making love with the Divine, sexual manifesting, sexual healing, and sexual play with creativity, polarity, and celebration of life. I am a yes to integrating all aspects of myself, including my shadows, and embracing the fullness of my identity as a multidimensional being. I am a yes to the inner union of feminine and masculine, radical responsibility, and sacred partnership with deep trust and intimacy. I am a yes to being deliciously and unapologetically deviant from what society wants me to be. I am a yes to creating and living the most extraordinary, expansive, inspiring, authentic life I can imagine that I am completely and utterly in love with. I am a yes to taking as long as I need for arousal, foreplay, and sensuality in intimacy. I am a yes to a partner who cherishes me, is committed to growth, takes accountability, invests in themselves and with me, sets and respects boundaries, and communicates openly and vulnerably.

2.   What are you a yes to?

RESOURCES:

The Wheel of Consent website by Betty Martin at www.bettymartin.org contains free educational videos that discuss important dimensions of consent, boundary setting, and identifying authentic desires within various combinations of partner dynamics. I can't recommend this resource enough for establishing safety, personal accountability, personal power, and integrity when engaging in touch with a partner.

DESIRES

———— ·~·~· ————

For a long time, I was not connected to my deepest desires because I was afraid of asking for too much and being rejected. When I wasn't suppressing my desires, I expected my partner to read my mind and just know what to do. I always had a strong sense of sexuality but I didn't always prioritize my own pleasure or know how to recognize and communicate my desires effectively. Despite being somewhat aware of my own sexuality, I still fell into patterns of self-abandoning and defaulting into making my partner happy. As I continued to learn and grow, I tried to express when I wanted something different, but I often didn't know how to communicate it. I could recognize when something didn't feel right, but I couldn't always pinpoint what I *did* want. And of course, it would change all the time depending on the moment and the circumstances I was in. Many times, my desire felt like a mystery to me and it was hard to identify the things that got a green light vs. a red one. This felt confusing, and the only way I could make sense of it was for my partner to change, which looked a lot like blaming as my communication was often critical or demanding.

My solo sex practice helped me identify what arouses me. Exploring independently allowed me to get to know my body, sensuality, and sexual fantasies without distractions or the influence of another person. This helped me learn more about what I wanted from a partner and intimacy. I got familiar with my desires by giving myself permission to play with my imagination, as well as inviting the Divine to energetically penetrate and work through me. My fantasies gave me clarity about how I want to be initiated and what helps me be open to receiving. I've learned that my desire is primarily responsive and it is my responsibility to identify and communicate what I need to feel connected and aroused.

This understanding was validated when I learned about the Dual Control Model of Sexual Response (developed by Dr. John Bancroft and Dr. Erick Janssen) discussed in Emily Nagoski's book, *Come As You Are.* In the book, Nagoski describes different types of sexual desire, including spontaneous desire, contextual desire (context matters), and responsive sexual desire which is affected by both exciters and inhibitors (like accelerators and brakes rather than just being a spontaneous "drive"). It was also empowering to recognize I am capable of creating scenarios and stimuli that evoke my own desire and arousal. This is where those Erotic Blueprints come in handy as they can help define what kinds of stimuli are arousing. When I am not entirely depending on my partner to elicit my desire, but I can partner with them and co-create situations that are mutually fulfilling, it relieves a lot of pressure from intimacy. Of course, I want to feel desire for my partner and to be desired by my partner, but when it's paired with pressure or demanding, it actually stifles intimacy.

There have been times I wanted to be approached differently, but I resented feeling like I had to teach my partner how to touch me. It took me out of the moment and into my head when I was focused on explaining. Everything changed when I realized the difference between explaining and expressing. I don't have to tell my partner what to do or explain how to approach me. I can express what I desire to experience and connect to the things I enjoy. The key to expression is being connected to both the feeling and my body. For example, I could *explain* to my partner that I want to be initiated assertively. I could define what assertive means and give examples of specific things that I would like to see. Or, I could *express* my desires in a fun game of foreplay as I give a detailed description of the ways I want my partner to touch me. I might express how excited it makes me when he grabs me from behind and pulls me into him, the way it takes my breath away when he kisses me deeply, and the way it melts me when I feel his breath against my neck and his hands around my waist with intention and presence. When I connect to the feeling and the desire, it feels exciting to invite him into each of those things. My focus and energy are going into creating an experience I desire instead of making a demand or setting an expectation.

Expression of desires does not always happen with verbal language. Sometimes it is through gestures, facial expressions, sounds, or literal movements pulling my partner into the experience I desire. My hands might be guiding his or collaborating alongside him as we stoke my desire and build my arousal together. I might give him feedback about things I like as I express pleasure in whatever form feels right. I might moan at his touch, press my body toward him, or pull him closer to me. Communicating desires does not have to be hard or stressful; it can be fun, creative, and sexy.

When I am in my expression, I am visualizing things I desire and imagining the feeling of doing or receiving it as I share. This makes expressing desire pleasurable in and of itself. It's inviting my creativity into connection and intimacy. It also requires flexibility and adaptability as my partner and I explore where we can both connect authentically. The intention of intimacy is to experience pleasure and create intimacy together. If either of us come into it with expectations or rigidity, it will significantly limit what we are able to experience. Often, rigidity creates a context for yes or no and leaves very little room for maybe. I like to think of expressing desire as a playful negotiation. It may start out with a seductive gesture or invitation, and might be met by enthusiastic response, a counter offer, or suggestion. Of course, there will be times when the answer really is a simple no. It doesn't need explanation or negotiation. I realize how important this is, especially in the context of consent. However, if we both understand that inviting each other is a reach for connection, without pressure or expectation, it is much easier to respond with love and affection.

These concepts aren't mutually exclusive. When I feel safe and respected in my no, I'm much more likely to give maybes and be open to exploration. I need a foundation of trust and safety that there won't be pressure or expectations from my partner to say yes when they express a desire and invite me to connect. If my partner initiates me and I am not a yes to that particular thing, I might pause to consider what I am open to experiencing. I might ask myself what I have the capacity to give and what I would desire in that moment to feel connected. Maybe I desire to be alone and suggest we connect at a later time. Maybe I desire to connect but am not open to the sexual invitation, so I suggest non-sexual touch or quality time instead. Or perhaps I do want sexual play, but I need help building my arousal first. This is especially relevant in the context of responsive sexual desire. I can want the idea of sex before I feel like my body actually wants it. When it comes to expressing desires and communication, it is all about the exchange. We will both take turns expressing desires in our own way and we can negotiate the roles we each want to play. Expressing desire doesn't have to mean requesting things you'd like to receive; it might also involve expressing desires for things you would like to initiate and do.

In order for this exchange to be healthy and possible, we need a foundation of consent where expression of desires in this way is welcome. Otherwise, it can feel like a violation of the other person's boundaries and create a context that doesn't feel safe or respectful (e.g., someone sending an unsolicited message with explicit content for their own benefit). We also both need to be able to effectively set boundaries and say no without taking it personally. It's important to recognize the street goes both ways, regardless of gender or sex. This was eye-opening for me when I realized I was unconsciously using sex as a source of validation. If my partner desired me and initiated, I was associating it with being lovable and good enough. I was making the same meaning of my partner saying yes to me when I would initiate. On the flip side, if my partner wasn't showing desire for me, I felt rejected and unloved. If I got a no when I initiated, I felt like something was wrong with me. In either situation, whether it was a yes or a no, I was taking it personally. When I felt rejected, I would respond with anger and hurt, closing off my body and heart with defensive walls. That's a lot of pressure to put on someone. When I release my fears of rejection and accept that my partner can say no to anything I ask for without making it mean anything about me, I can express my desires from a place of inviting rather than expecting.

JOURNAL PRACTICE:

Consider the following prompts regarding your sensual and/or sexual desires. For a playful twist, get descriptive and write your desires as though it were for your partner–like a written erotica piece.

1. *One thing I desire to experience sexually with a partner is...*

2. *One thing I am curious about exploring sexually with a partner is...*

3. *One thing I can do to be more open about my desires is...*

4. *Expressing my sexual desires to my partner feels...*

5. *When my partner does not share my sexual desire, I feel...*

6. *If I am not in the mood to engage sexually, one thing I would likely be open to instead is...*

7. *Telling my partner when I don't share their sexual desire feels...*

8. *One thing I can do to help myself with this feeling is...*

9. *One thing my partner can do to help me with this feeling is...*

RESOURCES:

Learn more about the Dual Control Model of Sexual Response (including questionnaires to help you learn more about your own sexual exciters and inhibitors) along with an incredible overview of research related to female sexuality that is informative, relatable, and applicable in Emily Nagoski's book, *Come As You Are.*

SACRED UNION

Inviting a lover into my sacred sexuality practice is incredibly vulnerable. It requires so much more than getting physically naked with a partner. First, I had to learn how to be emotionally and physically naked with myself. Once I was able to do that, I was able to expand the practice with my partner. Intimacy is a practice in vulnerability, which can have many degrees depending on the level of safety I feel. For me, there are two components to vulnerability: willingness and ability. I have to be willing to take emotional risks and share my vulnerability, open my heart, and invite a lover to join me. This is only possible if the context I am in provides the safety to be seen and held, as the person I'm with can recognize and respond to my vulnerability in an affirming way. I have experienced relationships that were not safe for vulnerability. I had to learn how to set my boundaries according to the level of trust and safety I felt with that person and express my needs. The good news is, trust and safety can be built, grown, and cultivated if both partners are willing. It can be a process requiring patience, time, and consistency to develop.

Interestingly, vulnerability breeds vulnerability. I have learned through experience and attachment theory that secure relationships are built through consistent reaching and responding to one another's vulnerability. When my partner and I are both taking emotional risks to be vulnerable and responding supportively, it builds mutual trust and safety. If I share my vulnerability and feel abandoned or rejected by my partner, it's harder to continue opening up. The same is true for my partner. It can take time to learn how to respond to my partner in a way that feels safe and supportive and for my partner to learn what I need. When we both feel safe to express ourselves and be vulnerable, it creates space for authenticity. It requires patience, compassion, and willingness to repair together when we miss the mark. The more I am able to express and share my authentic self, the more I can open myself to being seen and held in a sacred space with my partner. Sacred space intimacy can be experienced in degrees, based on the degree of vulnerability and safety we both receive.

There is a reason this section came after discussing personal accountability and radical responsibility in relationships. Vulnerability is not demanding, criticizing, blaming, recoiling, defending, placating, or reacting. It is my job to notice any reactivity or uncomfortable emotion I am experiencing and express it, but also own it. My reactivity is about me. It helps me identify what I am feeling and guides me to what I need. Sometimes what I need is an apology or acknowledgement of a boundary violation. I might express that I feel defensive, judged, angry, hurt, anxious, scared, abandoned, rejected, jealous, guarded, discouraged, or insecure. I can also express what I need to feel and ask for help to get there.

It is my responsibility to take care of my nervous system, take breaks when I need them, and ask for help. I am committed to helping my partner feel safe to the best of my ability and taking accountability for the impact of my actions. My partner is committed to the same. This is key because our intentions don't always align with our impact. Acknowledgement and sincerity can go a long way for repairing when these moments happen. Taking each other's perspective with compassion, validating each other's experience, and recognizing the impact we have on each other builds a foundation of love and safety that invites vulnerability. We won't always get it right, but we are committed to learning and growing from our mistakes and returning to love every time.

We also take responsibility for our own raw spots and reactivity. Everyone has their own version of emotional baggage they bring into a relationship. Sometimes that baggage is super useful and supportive of creating intimacy. Other times it involves unhealed wounds, scars, and defense mechanisms that override vulnerability and block intimacy. Raw spots for me might include wounds I've experienced from past romantic partners, parents, or other life experiences. My internal model for what to expect from relationships, how I handle vulnerability, and how I give and receive love is shaped by my life experiences and what they taught me. I didn't get to choose all of my life experiences and I had to learn adaptive responses. While I may have needed certain strategies in the past to survive, they do not all serve me in the present. When these ineffective strategies show up now, they can help me recognize which places need healing.

Healing my wounds is my responsibility, but that doesn't mean I have to do it alone. In fact, I can't do it alone. After all, these wounds were created in the context of relationships so it only makes sense that they also need to be healed in a relational context. As social creatures, we all need help and connection. This is one of the most beautiful aspects of sacred union. It gets to be a healing container for both of us to create and show up in, if we both choose it. When both partners are willing to take responsibility for themselves, it creates a sense of mutual wholeness. Codependency is born of two halves coming together and feeling whole, which creates a narrative that they are dependent on each other for survival. Interdependence is two wholes coming together and creating something new and expansive through the union. It is the recognition that I am both whole on my own and wired for connection. Part of this mentality includes the awareness of interconnectedness between all people and all things. With this understanding, I am capable of getting my needs met through a variety of sources as a part of a larger collective. When I do not depend on my partner to meet all of my needs, it gives me a sense of freedom to choose who I partner with. Freedom to choose gives more power to the choice. It also creates more opportunity for intention and purpose vs. survival or necessity. It allows it to serve a higher goal and dedicates the union to a higher purpose, vision, shared intention, and creation. What can you we co-create as conscious beings?

The other cool thing about sacred union is there is no single blueprint to what it needs to look like. Relationships come in many forms, and sacred space can be created between any combination of people. I have found the consistent components required for a sacred space interaction are safety, respect, trust, compassion, vulnerability, presence, accountability, integrity, willingness, and sovereignty. I have experienced incredible healing, intimacy, and depth in groups and communities where these values are shared and upheld. I've stood in the center of a room surrounded by fifty other people as I expressed deeply raw vulnerability and felt safe, seen, and held because of the container we had created together. I've held friends while they sobbed in my lap because they felt safe enough to let themselves break and release the pain they had been carrying. I've screamed at the top of my lungs, rage burning through my body, tears streaming down my cheeks, as I was witnessed by a trusted brother who reflected nothing but compassion and love through his gaze. I've grieved generations of sexual repression and body shame with my sisters, danced barefoot under the stars in celebration of life with a soul tribe, and swam naked in the ocean with friends to reclaim the innocence of our bodies.

I've had a sister place her hands on my back and chest, holding my heart as it was breaking in grief. I've had a partner hold my hand in the middle of the night as I whispered my first prayer out loud to the Divine after my faith crisis. Once, when I was sobbing in my sleep, my partner wrapped himself around me and gently woke me to ask, "Would you like to have a different dream?" I've witnessed people share their stories of surviving sexual abuse, trauma, grief, loss, and shame, and the resilience that they've built along the way. Others have shared their sexual identity, gender identity, and spiritual gifts for the very first time, their voices layered with the fear of being seen and exercising the courage to share anyway. I've felt my soul merge with my lover as we moved in unison and became like liquid together. I've experienced miracles, Divine intervention, synchronicities, and tender moments so sacred they are difficult to capture in words. Each of these experiences has been possible because of co-created sacred spaces.

Sexuality is another dimension of sacred union, with an embodiment of emotional intimacy that exists in these kinds of naked moments. It is an act of giving and receiving love, an exchange of energy, a co-created connection, and an embodiment of Divine Love. Sexual intimacy in sacred union is an opportunity to open ourselves to experiencing the Divine through our exchange. If there is not a foundation of safety, trust, and vulnerability, it is impossible to create a sacred space with a partner. If I don't feel safe enough to express my desires, fears, or needs, I won't be able to experience the depth of intimacy that I truly desire. If I choose not to express vulnerability with my partner, I am not allowing myself to be fully seen. I see intimacy as a lifelong journey of deepening with myself in the context of my relationships, both romantically and platonically. When the foundation is set, I can trust myself and my partner, I can express my needs, desires, and fears, I am open to receiving love and affection, and I am willing to hold space for my partner's truth without taking it personally.

What does sacred union mean to me? It is both people being willing to show up in their authenticity with open hearts and willingness to be seen. It is a co-creation of a sacred space between lovers with trust, safety, honest communication, mutual respect, and integrity. I define sacred as something that is precious, personal, and devoted to God (with God meaning love in the highest form). In the same way we open our hearts to pray, intimacy requires vulnerability to give and receive love to that degree. Intimacy can be a sacred practice, sharing our most vulnerable parts with another. My solo sex practice is like an embodied prayer. It is an exchange with the Divine, opening my heart, mind, body, and soul to giving and receiving love. Practicing love for myself, receiving compassion and support from the Divine, and expressing love, gratitude, and devotion in return. This practice allows me to feel closer to God and to become one with love. In his book *Dear Lover*, David Deida wrote about sexual intimacy as "two-bodied love." He describes a concept of lovemaking as devotion to love itself, with the exchange between two lovers being energy dedicated to healing the world. This is how I define sacred sexuality. A devotion to love. A healing exchange through corrective experiences. A celebration of life. I can practice it alone as an embodied prayer or magnify it through a two-bodied prayer in sacred union.

Sexuality is what allowed me to be fully surrendered in my feminine and held by a masculine lover (who was a man in this case). Connected to my body, my heart, and the Divine, I received him into my yoni as he held me close and expressed the most beautiful words from his heart to mine. I have never felt more seen, cherished, or loved in my life. It was so powerful that it was almost more than I could take in. My heart had been so hurt before–could I let myself believe him? In that moment, I felt my heart expand its capacity to receive. After years of guarding my heart, fearing I was too much or not enough, and terrified of being deeply known and seen for fear that my partner might reject or leave me, this was a new level of vulnerability. Deep in my being, I knew he was sincere and expressing from a place of integrity. It was safe to receive. I melted into the love and fully embodied it. I breathed it into my core and expanded it through my heart. Everything in me softened and opened at the same time.

To create sacred spaces in sexuality, not only do I need to de-armor my physical tension to open with a partner, I also need to de-armor emotionally. This can take time as safety and trust are built. It can be an exploration of authenticity, with each of us discerning what we feel ready to share and experience and to what degree. It's a co-creation of intimacy through authentic relating. One of the most effective tools I have experienced to create this kind of sacred space with a lover is through eye-gazing, breathing in synchrony, and close proximity with touch like holding hands or straddling each other (my favorite).

This process of co-regulation helps my body feel safe to soften into the connection. I embrace the connection with mindful observation of my internal experience. I take note of what I am thinking, feeling, and sensing. I move slowly and honor my own pace. I try to create a calm state of safety and openness in my own body and heart, and attune to my own needs.

When I am able to stay connected to myself and my own needs, I am much more able to create authentic connection with my partner. This allows me to prevent old patterns of people-pleasing from creeping in which can involve hyper-focusing on the feelings of my partner, and self-abandoning. If I am present within my own authenticity, I am more capable of holding space for my partner to share their feelings and needs without taking it personally. I am also more capable of responding with love, presence, sincerity, compassion, and generosity to my partner's desires and needs. These are all authentic qualities that come naturally when my heart is open and connected to love and safety. When my partner and I practice this, we are creating a space for both of us to engage and share openly, supporting each other to feel safe in our vulnerability. We are practicing honoring our own and each other's boundaries so when we do engage, we can trust that it's something we are both enthusiastically choosing.

I feel more comfortable expressing my desires and needs when there is a foundation of safety and I can trust my partner to respond with respect, love, and integrity with their boundaries. It is easier to share kinks, fantasies, desires, and vulnerable feelings when we are both committed to being a safe container for each other. I commit to not judging, shaming, or rejecting my partner's vulnerability, and being honest with my own truth and boundaries. My partner can express any desire or need and I will respond lovingly without being obligated to meet the need or engage in something that doesn't feel authentic to me. I can be honest about what I have capacity for, what I am responsible for, and what I desire to experience. Either of us are entitled to feel anything that comes up within us without fear of judgment. When I practice radical responsibility, I am taking ownership of my reactions, triggers, judgments, and needs. I won't always be able to meet my partner's needs, and they won't always be able to meet mine. That is a reality of life. Intimacy isn't always easy. Vulnerability isn't always comfortable. But the connection that is possible as a result of creating those sacred space moments is absolutely worth the investment.

Slowing down is crucial. I have to slow down my responding, thought processing, observing, communicating, and listening. Being fully present and connected in a moment requires me to be tuned in to myself with awareness of my body, my emotions, my desires, and my needs. It also requires me to be attuned to my partner to receive what they are expressing and respond intentionally. It sounds like a lot to pay attention to at once, and it certainly can be, but that isn't a bad thing. When I give attention to nuances like this and slow down to notice them, I get to see the beauty and opportunity in each element. My pleasure expands as I connect more deeply to myself. The connection is richer and deeper when my partner feels seen, heard, and respected.

As we both engage with open hearts, we embody the Divine within us. I allow myself to be a conduit for Divine Love to express through me, and I surrender my heart, mind, and body to the moment. In moments like these, I experience a deeper awareness of the interconnectedness of all things. My consciousness is not separate from God or my lover, but instead, we are one–dancing together. This dance allows the union of our bodies to represent the union of our life force energies, our consciousness intertwining.

In earlier chapters, the concepts of shadow work, radical self-acceptance, authentic identity, and inner polarity were discussed. As we expand our connection to include another person, the same principles can apply as we explore dynamics and experiences to express ourselves and create an energetic exchange. Sexuality is a form of adult play. Through this lens, the possibilities are endless for what we can create, limited only by our imagination and a shared desire with a partner. I can explore the nuances of my masculine, feminine, wild, reserved, playful, powerful, assertive, shy, dominant, submissive, kinky, sweet, sensual, innocent, tender, animalistic, taboo, vanilla, passionate, or anything and everything expression within sacred union. I can express the desires of my heart and body and create experiences just for the fun of it or for incredibly deep healing. The most important thing is, I can be everything and anything I want to be. I have the power to create my inner world and decide which parts to express and engage with my lover, based on the exchange that is authentic and co-created. We can share something completely unique and beautiful as we work and play together.

One of the truths I have discovered in my own exploration is there is power in polarity. Polarity creates an energetic charge between us. I have found it is a principle of sexual attraction, but it doesn't have to be fixed or stagnant. I define who I am on the inside and what feels authentic to express in the context of my relationship. Sexuality is not something to be confined to boxes. It is creative energy. It is sacred energy. It is sovereign energy. My sexual energy is a power that belongs to me, for me to define and play with. The same is true for my partner. When we combine resources and life force energy in sacred union, we get to play with the power of polarity. We get to create combinations of polarity that are powerful, meaningful, pleasurable, fun, and dynamic. There is no right or wrong way for this to play out. If it feels authentic to us to have consistent roles and enjoy the pleasure and gifts of that pairing, great! If we desire to switch it up and add variety and novelty in the different scenarios we create, also great! There is depth and beauty that can be found in each experience, and every person is entitled to their own definition of authentic desire.

I'd like to speak about some shifts in the traditional roles of polarity between men and women in heterosexual pairings. The role of men is changing in this new age of empowered women. Men are being called to step up and take accountability for their own healing as the bar for integrity, self-awareness, and emotional intimacy is rising.

Conscious, evolved men do not fear empowered women but support them, partner with them, encourage them, cherish and honor them, respect them, protect them, love them, listen to them, and advocate for them. Conscious men celebrate empowered women because empowered women are free women. Liberating women from oppression is also a step toward liberating men from being oppressive. I don't see balance coming from women becoming hypermasculine and men becoming hyperfeminine. I see balance coming from all people healing both aspects within themselves and becoming whole and integrated within. We live in a heteronormative society, even with the recent years of LGBTQIA+ advocacy. The healing work doesn't stop with men treating women with equality and inclusivity and replacing toxic gender expectations. It doesn't stop with women doing their healing work of empowering themselves and each other and replacing toxic gender expectations.

The healing work continues in how men treat other men, how women treat other women, and how we all treat anyone who doesn't fit the traditional mold of socially constructed gender or sexuality expectations. We can all do better at creating a safer and more inclusive place for LBGTQIA+ people as they define their own authentic expression. We can liberate the oppressed and become less oppressive as we change the culture we all participate in. Together we can heal the narrative we have been stuck in, break the cycles that have been passed down for generations, and write a new story of sacred union, within and between.

JOURNAL PRACTICE:

1. How have you experienced a sacred space in your life? If you can't think of one, how might you want to experience it?

2. How do you define sacred union?

3. What role does polarity play in your life?

RESOURCES:

For additional exercises that promote physical and emotional intimacy, consider exploring tantric practices. A great book on this is *The Art of Sexual Ecstasy* by Margot Anand.

SEXUAL HEALING

Sexual energy is powerful. Like any power, it can cause harm or healing. As I have reclaimed my own power, it has allowed me to experience incredible healing. Through sacred sexuality practices, I have healed my relationship to the Divine, my body, myself, and people I love. I have found physical, mental, emotional, and spiritual healing through orgasms and the power of my pleasure. When I get stuck in cycles of burnout, stress, anxiety, or depression, I have learned to listen to my body's wisdom and use its sensitivity to bring more balance to my life. Understanding my body has helped me embrace the natural fluctuations that are part of life with more ease and grace. It has helped me see the wisdom in my embodied feminine nature and the gifts of accepting myself in all of my phases. Liberating my sexual self and practicing radical acceptance woke me up to my spiritual magic. Only two years ago, I would have told you I am not a naturally creative person. I would have told you I struggle to feel inspired and feel shut down in my self-expression. Balancing my sacral chakra, healing my sexual wounds, and (I can't emphasize this enough) devoting to my solo sex practice opened me up to my creative gifts and a heightened spiritual intuition. It was the key to unlocking the wisdom of my body that I had been missing.

Through my own process of radical acceptance and self-love, I have learned to regulate my nervous system and respond to triggers from emotional wounds. I have been able to heal the root of many of these wounds and use my sacred sexuality practices to maintain the healing and reinforce the new truths. In sacred union with partners in my current and past relationships, we have healed childhood wounds through being an embodiment of love in each other's life. I've made significant progress with understanding my attachment style and the underlying needs of my inner child. I have learned to respond to her with love and reach for support from loving relationships with family, friends, therapists, coaches, and my partner. The patterns of people-pleasing or criticizing have been replaced with vulnerability and authenticity, allowing me to experience deeper and more fulfilling intimacy.

When my partner and I allow ourselves to be truly vulnerable, seen, and loved, there are no words for the healing power of those sacred space exchanges. My experience of love has been expanded exponentially through learning to love myself, grow in love with the Divine, and the practice of giving and receiving in my relationships with others.

My partner and I are both able to engage in the healing work of ourselves and each other through creating corrective experiences with our connection. Together we can rewire beliefs that don't serve us and write new narratives about spirituality, relationships, love, sexuality, and the meaning of life. We can create a shared life purpose, amplify abundance through combining shared resources, manifest dreams, create our own reality, build community, embrace our humanity, experience all the joys and pleasures of being alive, and redefine what it means to be one with the Divine.

Doing this work has been the most difficult and rewarding process of my life. Healing has been my life's work. But as I have learned the tools that have brought me relief from suffering and balance through the pleasure of creation, healing is no longer something I do while I wait to start living. I enjoy my life and see pain as part of the process. I'm excited about the possibilities of what I get to create and experience. I welcome my inner child with open arms as I seek opportunities to play and she brings her wisdom of imagination, creativity, and finding joy in the journey. My spirituality and sexuality are now the most rewarding, enriching, and vibrant aspects of my life. They have given me the tools to create deep and meaningful relationships, a fulfilling life purpose and passion, and a sense of connection to humanity and the world around me. I'm grateful for the Divine grace, support, and guidance I have received from my spiritual team and I feel incredibly lucky to be alive.

RESOURCES:

For more information and tools related to emotional intimacy, attachment healing, and corrective experiences in relationships, I'd recommend the following books:

- *Hold Me Tight: Seven Conversations for a Lifetime of Love* by Dr. Sue Johnson

- *Wired for Love: How Understanding Your Partner's Brain and Attachment Style Can Help You Defuse Conflict and Build a Secure Relationship* by Stan Tatkin, PsyD

- *Use Your Mouth: Pocket-sized Conversations to Simply Increase 7 Types of Intimacy in and out of the Bedroom* by sexologist Shamyra Howard, LCSW

CLOSING THOUGHTS

I couldn't have gotten to where I am now without redefining my spirituality. I had to heal the wounds that were created from my spiritual abuse and indoctrination from an oppressive religion. I had to heal my relationship with the Divine, my body, feminine and masculine energy, and my own authentic identity. I had to reclaim my inner voice of authority to restore my own intuition as my source of personal revelation. I had to give myself permission to explore what had previously been forbidden to discern for myself what I believe in. I strongly disagree with many of the teachings in my childhood. I feel fortunate to have the opportunity to spare my own children from going through the same experience I did. I have no interest in telling them who to be, but I have every intention to raise them with the tools to connect within themselves and their inner knowing to decide for themselves how to live. I plan to teach them a variety of philosophies and perspectives, including ideologies from religion. If they choose to follow religion as they get older, I will support them on their own path of discovery and be at peace knowing they were given a foundation of freedom to choose with resources to develop critical thinking and sovereignty.

As for my inner child, I am still healing. I am still learning to prioritize her and give her the loving support and consistency she needs. I am much more selective with my inner circle of close relationships, but especially in sacred union and intimate partnership. My relationship with my feminine and masculine is highly important to me as an integrated being. I also value polarity in my relationships as I embody multiple dimensions of my identity and encourage my partner to do the same.

Sexuality is no longer wrapped in shame, but rather something I openly nurture and celebrate. Intimacy requires vulnerability that provides opportunities for deep connection and healing. I now have a fulfilling relationship with myself, humanity, and the Divine. I've never felt more alive, more loving, or more creative in my life. As you continue your own exploration of the topics and ideas discussed in this book, I pray that you find liberation, sovereignty, expansion, connection, peace, clarity, and above all, pleasure and ecstasy beyond your wildest dreams.

RESOURCES:

I hope you have found the journal prompts and resources in this book to be helpful for your journey to discovering your authentic self, expanding your sexuality and spirituality, and healing from emotional suffering. As much as self-help exercises and practices can be powerful tools, they cannot replace being held in a safe container to process with someone you trust. I would not be where I am today without the support of therapy with trained professionals, coaching, healing retreats, authentic community, friends, family, and partners.

In my opinion and experience, the best approach is holistic (treating the whole person in context of their environment) and integrated (bio-psycho-social-spiritual-environmental) health care. Ideally, this includes natural supports like positive relationships, joyful movement practices, spiritual resources, creative outlets, and community involvement as well as professional supports like trauma-informed physical health care with a blend of western and eastern methods (including cellular detox, nutrition, and nervous system support), and trauma-informed mental and emotional health care. If you are seeking more support in these areas, I encourage you to seek professional support to help you. I have a personal bias for embodiment practices because they have led to the most personal transformation, but I do believe they were more effective when I had also developed self-awareness of my thoughts, beliefs, emotions, and behaviors that weren't serving me and where they came from. I recommend the following modalities, as they have been highly effective for my own healing process:

For trauma healing:

Coaching does not replace what a trained therapist can provide. While they both have extraordinary value, it is important for each person to discern for themselves what type and level of support they need. I have relied on both to get where I am now. As a licensed therapist and relationship coach, I value both as tools for healing and achieving transformative results.

Somatic Experiencing is a body-oriented therapeutic model that helps heal trauma and other stress disorders. Eye Movement Desensitization and Reprocessing (EMDR) is an effective, efficient psychotherapy model to help process and heal from intense negative emotional experiences and traumatic events.

For nervous system support, you can try breathwork, yoga, dance or other somatic release tools, cryotherapy (cold showers, ice baths, sauna), red light therapy, compression therapy, sound healing, time in nature, holistic nutrition, medication (when applicable), creative outlets, community involvement with positive connections, crying, long hugs, and support animals (officially or unofficially), just to name a few. Learn about how to complete the "stress response cycle" and activate the parasympathetic nervous system to counteract the impact of chronic stress states in the body.

Not everyone has the resources to access all forms of care, but there are many ways to practice these tools and build positive relationships or community involvement at little to no cost. This is something a coach or therapist can help you strategize in your unique area according to your needs and circumstances. If you have limited resources, I hope these recommendations can help maximize the quality of your care as you invest in your healing and find the right providers for you.

<u>If you are seeking a therapist for attachment healing and relationship work:</u>

Emotionally Focused Therapy (EFT) is very effective for couples or individual work, including Hold Me Tight workshops for an immersive introduction to the work and a solid foundation to work from. If this is not available to you in your area, there are virtual workshops available, and you can work with any professional who is well-versed in attachment theory. The Psychobiological Approach to Couples Therapy (PACT) is another fantastic modality for powerful corrective experiences in relational work.

<u>For spiritual wellness (anything that helps you tune in to yourself, your intuition, and your own spiritual gifts and revelations):</u>

If you choose to work on spirituality goals in therapy, it is important to know you have a right to choose your provider and to receive unbiased support for your spiritual beliefs and lifestyle choices. A good provider will allow you to define your own values and will not project their own beliefs onto you, even if they differ from yours. You can shop around for the right therapist and find someone you feel comfortable with who can support you in discerning what is right for you.

Yoga: Classic vinyasa flows and deep restorative practices. Yoga with Adriene on YouTube has classes designed for PTSD healing specifically. You can start on your own with online classes, but my favorite is an in-person class for a more potent experience practicing alongside others in community.

Meditation: My favorite way to start is through guided meditation. There are many free apps you can download. My preference is Insight Timer and my favorite facilitator is Sarah Blondin, though I also love exploring the app and I discover new favorites all the time!

Sound healing: Crystal or Tibetan singing bowls, gong baths, drums, a combination of instruments curated for healing, chanting or mantra singing like Kirtan, or healing frequency music. My favorite is creating my own intuitively, playing music with friends in community, or listening to music from inspired artists in any genre that resonates for me.

Energy medicine: Body Talk, Ayurveda, Light Healing, imagery, breathwork, etc. My go-to resource for energy work is Terra@terraroseganem.com. She has changed my life in ways I can't even begin to express.

Breathwork: There are various types of breathwork modalities for different purposes. I have experienced Kundalini, Shamanic, and Holotropic breathwork and they have all been transformative. One of my trusted mentors describes her method as "expansion through connecting the intangible and tangible with the breath."

Coaching: I'm a big fan of group coaching and in-person retreats with immersive experiential practices and a community-oriented model for healing. I offer coaching groups and retreats for women to deepen their relationship with themselves, the Divine, and each other in a non-judgmental, supportive community environment. I've also worked with incredible coaching mentors on my path to finding my spiritual home within myself. There are many opportunities like this available, and different ones will resonate differently depending on where you are in your healing journey.

Nature is a medicine and teacher for the mind, body, and soul. Holistic nutrition, naturopathy, plant medicine, and shamanic journeys have been helpful modalities for my physical and energetic healing. Equally powerful practices have been swimming in the ocean, walking barefoot on grass or bare earth, gardening with my hands in the soil and eating home grown food, soaking in sunshine, hiking in forests or red rocks, rock climbing, kayaking, witnessing sunrises and sunsets, and being surrounded by trees, flowers, and green as much as humanly possible.

A great resource for those navigating a faith transition from religion is a book called *Leaving Religion & Those We Leave Behind: A guidebook for navigating the waters after leaving religion & finding your spiritual center* by Amanda Joy Loveland.

For Sexual Wellness

AASECT certified therapists are often more specialized with a higher level of training and experience in treating sexual challenges. This certification isn't required for quality care in overcoming sexual challenges, but depending on what your goals are, it may be helpful to find a provider with specialized training. Similar to finding a therapist for spirituality goals, whoever you work with should be affirming, knowledgeable, and supportive of your identity, orientation, and lifestyle choices without projecting their own beliefs or judgments. You should feel safe and free to express yourself as long as you are engaging in a respectful manner that is appropriate for the boundaries and agreements within the professional working relationship. You should never feel obligated or pressured to discuss details of your sexuality that you are not comfortable sharing. It is never appropriate for a therapist to engage in sexual activity with a client due to the ethical limits of their license.

Tantric workshops and modalities are very helpful in developing a deeper connection to yourself, your partner(s), and your spirituality through sensual and sexual practices. There are many options to explore from books to retreats, workshops, and personal massage and coaching sessions. There are fewer restrictions and regulations with coaching of any kind, which can create more opportunities for the kinds of healing experiences that can be created. This freedom also comes with more personal responsibility to exercise your judgment and sovereignty when deciding who to work with. This can be very empowering to define your own boundaries, set goals, express desires, and receive support for deep embodied healing.

All in all, choosing the right coaches and mentors has been easy when I am rooted in my intuition and sovereignty. It's the same as choosing a gynecologist. If I don't trust them to be respectful, sensitive, and supportive of me as the expert of my own body, they aren't going anywhere near my yoni (metaphorically or literally). Whether it is a spiritual coach, intimacy coach, or business coach, it needs to be a yes in my heart, mind, body, and yoni.

ARE YOU READY TO DIVE DEEPER?

If you'd like to receive coaching support from me, email me directly at julie3mft@gmail.com for details on how to work with me individually, participate in my Sacred Sexuality Mastermind, or attend one of my upcoming embodiment and sensuality retreats!

Join my mailing list for additional information, resources, and future offerings by following the link below and get a bonus gift exclusively for my readers!

https://julie-elizabeth.mykajabi.com/book-email-opt-in

You can also follow me on Instagram: @julieb_livefree

Did you love this book? Was it helpful to you?

I would be so grateful if you could head over to Amazon,
or wherever you purchased this book from,
and leave a review!

Each review matters . . . a lot!

Thank you, thank you, thank you.

With love,

Julie

Made in United States
Orlando, FL
09 August 2022

20758103R00125